Breeding Pedigree Beef Cattle

Acknowledgements

I would like to thank everyone involved in producing this book for their contribution of encouragement, help and advice, especially the various Breed Societies and Breeders who supplied any facts, figures, or photographs requested.

R. Newcombe M.R.C.V.S. For suggesting and encouraging me to write the book in the first instance.

S.N.B. Bayer M.R.C.V.S. and P. Freeman M.R.C.V.S. For advice on veterinary matters.

D. Esmor Evans M.R.C.V.S. for encouragement and advice.

Jeff Marshall and Christine Marshall; for convincing me, that at sixty four, I was not too old for them to teach me how to use a word processor.

Sue Gerrard for technical advice.

My wife Christina; without her understanding and tolerance of the anti-social hours needed to be worked by a stockman to do his job properly, I would not have had so much pleasure being a stockman for the past forty-five years.

Breeding Pedigree Beef Cattle

Gordon Rugg

Published by Gordavian Books.

Published by Gordavian Books.
Home Farm, Great Totham, Maldon, Essex. CM9 8NU.
© 1997 Gordon Rugg.

British Library Cataloguing-in-Publication Data

Breeding Pedigree Beef Cattle Rugg, Gordon
ISBN 0 9529996 0 9

Graphic images; Frank Wognum, Airflow Design, Chelmsford, Essex.

Book design and digital layout; David Andrews Design, Little Bentley, Essex.

Reprographics and printing; Mayland Graphics, Maldon, Essex.

Contents

Introduction

There can be few things in life that give more satisfaction, or sense of achievement, than being a successful breeder of pedigree livestock, be it racehorses, cattle, sheep, pigs, dogs or whatever. The only trouble is that a lifetime is seldom long enough to achieve the ultimate aim of breeding the perfect animal.

Having worked as a stockman for the last forty-five years with pedigree beef breeds including; Beef Shorthorn, Aberdeen Angus, Highland, Galloway, Welsh Black, Charolais, and also fat stock show cattle, it was suggested that I should to put my experience on paper.

This I have tried to do, but I have made no attempt to make this book technical, and while it is written with the primary aim of giving those starting up a pedigree herd of beef cattle an insight as to what is involved, (in the hope that it will save them from learning from their mistakes), it should also be of interest to established pedigree and commercial cattle breeders.

The book is divided into three chapters. The first chapter deals with starting up the herd and general management, the second covers seasonal work, shows. sales and etiquette. While the third covers pedigrees, transport, faults, ailments, buildings and equipment.

Gordon Rugg

Chapter one

Starting up a herd

If you are thinking of starting up a herd of pedigree beef cattle you should first realise that the main source of income from it will be from the sale of bulls, which have to be reared and handled until they are about eighteen months of age. That standards of stockmanship are very high, with no place for any animal not brought out to its full potential. So unless you intend to employ an experienced stockman you must be prepared to put in a lot of time and effort for the venture to succeed.

My advice to those of you with no previous experience of breeding pedigree cattle would be; first research the different breeds, find out as much as you can about their different characteristics, then you can decide which breed is best suited to your style of management.

When you have decided, join the breed society of your choice. They will then send you a copy of their rules, the latest issue of their breed journal, containing reports of the major shows and sales, along with advertisements from the top breeders. This will give you an idea of the prices being paid for bulls, females, semen etc.

Next go to as many shows and sales as possible, and get aquainted with the breeders and stockmen so that when you are watching the judging with them you can ask their opinion as to why certain animals are placed top or bottom of their class. Note their comments in your catalogue to enable you to recognise the animals when they come into the sale ring. You will then see by the prices they make, which good features to look for, and which faults to keep clear of.

If you are starting up a fairly large herd, and are going to employ an experienced stockman, it is always best to employ the stockman right at the start, because if he has a say in buying the foundation females and any alterations to the buildings that need to be done, there is far more chance of the venture being a success.

If as a breeder of commercial stock thinking of replacing some of them with pedigree stock, be sure to discuss your intention thoroughly with your stockman, as not all stockmen working with commercial cattle want the extra work and attention to detail that is necessary when working with pedigree stock. Unless your stockman is one hundred percent in favour of the change and is prepared to make a go of it, there is little chance of success.

Before leaving the subject of experienced stockmen, I would advise inexperienced breeders to treat their stockman with respect. Form a good working relationship with him, based on a mutual trust, where each one's ideas are respected. When basic policy has been decided the stockman is then left to get on with the day-to-day running of the herd. It is also important to keep the stockman informed as to the financial standing of the herd, in this way he can arrange sales to suit cash flow needs.

I would also like to give a word of advice to any stockman reading this book. While most stockmen treat the animals in their care as if they own them, some go a bit too far, and forget who really does own the herd, as well as who pays the wages. So while it is essential that the stockman has his say, final decisions should always be left to the employer.

Stockmen should not only learn the skill of breeding, feeding, and showing cattle. They should also learn the art of handling employers and assistants, and how to fit in with other enterprises on the farm.

NB. *The term stockmen may not be politically correct in this day and age but as most of the top female stock attendants would rather be called stockmen than stockpersons, I will use the word stockmen throughout the book, with apologies to those who object.*

Buying foundation cattle

Females

It is most important when buying pedigree females, anywhere other than at official breed society sales, to ensure that the animals are registered in their respective herd book, that they are properly tattooed and that their mouths are inspected to make sure that the teeth on their lower jaw match the dental pad on the upper one, being neither undershot nor overshot, (***see figure A,B,C p. 68-9)***

There is no need to check cattle sold at official breed society sales. They are checked by the breed society inspectors to make sure their teeth are correct; that they are properly tattooed; and that their tattoo corresponds to the one entered in the catalogue. Some breed societies also check to make sure the animals are sound on their legs, but as it is very difficult for inspectors to know where to draw the line, I would strongly advise buyers to set their own standards and check the feet and legs on any animals they are thinking of buying, and to remember the saying "buyer beware".

There are several ways to go about buying females. It all depends on how much money is available, and how soon you want to get results, although it is worth remembering that success cannot be guaranteed no matter how much money is spent. If you want to be competitive right from the start, then you will need to buy the best you can find and be prepared to pay top prices for them, because, as with everything else, quality never comes cheap.

On the other hand if you are buying to a budget, or looking to the venture on a long term basis, a lot more skill and care is needed, and this is where advice from an experienced breeder or stockman is invaluable. The one thing to be aware of when starting up a herd, is the speed at which numbers will increase. For this reason it is best to set up a small nucleus of good cattle then add to it when the opportunity arises.

Females are very dominant in cattle breeding, and within herds there are families that breed well to any bull. It is often better to buy an average female from a good family, than a "one off" good one from a bad family. When buying females, bear in mind that it is always easier to reduce the size of animals by selective breeding than to increase it, so it is always best to buy animals with a bit of size, substance and character about them, to form the foundation of the herd. The best place to buy foundation females is at the dispersal of a successful, long established herd, where you know the animals are being sold for a genuine reason. As the whole herd is being sold, it is usually possible to see the progeny of the older cows, enabling you to figure out which are the best families.

Good cattle can also be picked up at herd reduction sales, where breeders reduce their herd size by holding a sale, either on their farm or at a cattle market in conjunction with a breed society event. This most often consists of a selection of mature females and often the whole crop of two-year-old in-calf heifers and possibly three-year-olds with calves at foot. While the older cows (except for one or two good ones entered as bait) are usually being sold because they have not come up to the vendor's standard, the three-year-olds and two-year-olds will be genuine, especially if the whole age group is being sold.

Another way of buying foundation females is to go to an established breeder and see if he will sell you some of his older cows, or two year old heifers in calf. If you do this, have someone with you who you can trust to value the animals for you, because while most breeders are trustworthy, there is always the unscrupulous one who will take a beginner "to the cleaners".

Make sure when you buy cattle this way, that you are offered the pick of the complete age group, otherwise, if the breeder is allowed to select the ones he is prepared to sell you, it is possible that you will end up with lot of second rate animals, as he is sure to keep the best ones for himself.

I would advise beginners with no previous experience of breeding any kind of cattle, to buy first or second calvers with calf at foot and in calf again, as this will not only save you the worry of having to calve heifers, but also give you a chance to get established much more quickly. If you start up with in-calf heifers and get a run of bad luck calving them, and then have trouble getting them back in calf, it can take a long time to get a return on the initial investment.

It is a great temptation when buying cows to go for the big fat ones, but as often as not, (except for cows that have been shown) the reason they look so well is that they have been idle most of their lives, through either having had dead calves, having been difficult to get in calf, or being poor milkers. Cows that breed regularly, and milk well, seldom get a chance to get too fat and may sometimes look a bit plain; their value can only be assessed by the quality of their off-spring.

Stock bulls

Buying stock bulls is a bit of a gamble, because no matter how good a young bull's mother and father were or how well it looks itself, there is no guarantee that it will leave calves that will be above average, but if it is out of a good family and by a good sire the chances of it breeding well, are increased.

Wherever possible stock bulls should be purchased from breeders who have a proven track record for breeding bulls that go on to be good herd sires. Again as with females, it is often better to buy an above average bull out of a good cow from a top herd, than a (one off) good one out of an average cow from a below-average herd. Attention should be taken of faults in any other bulls by the same sire as the one you are interested in that are in the consignment, because if they all have the same faults then it is almost certain to be hereditary.

Consideration has also to be given as to who fed the animal, as some stockmen are experts at bringing out bulls to be at the peak of perfection on the day of the sale, but as these bulls are fed into good ones, rather than being bred good ones, they are seldom heard of again.

One of the main considerations when buying a stock bull, is that it sound on it legs, and whether any faults it has are hereditary or the result of over-feeding. The second consideration is that it is up to size and of good conformation. It is rare for bulls to leave offspring that will grow up to be bigger than themselves, except when they are used on very large cows.

When talking about size, I should make it clear that I am talking about actual height and width and not simply weight, as there is a big difference between the two. Some little round bulls put on a lot of weight up to about 15 months of age but will then slow down and finish up below average size.

A stock bull's success should be judged by the average of its progeny, as there will be far more profit from a bull whose progeny are all sound and can all be sold for breeding, than one that produces the odd high-priced one with a lot of the others going for killing because they are bad on their legs or have some other fault.

Breeding policies and culling

Type
When deciding the type of animal to breed, bear in mind that most of the bulls sold at pedigree sales are sold to commercial breeders. At the same time it is worth remembering that heifers of the same type as the bull wanted by the commercial breeder may be a bit too neat for what is wanted to maintain the size in the pedigree herd.

To correct this it may be necessary to use a bull that is a bit more rugged every now and again, to retain the size in the replacement females. Avoid breeding extreme types as they are no use to any one, Try to build up a reputation for selling good sound cattle that go on to do well in their new homes.

Having purchased the foundation females, a decision has to be made as to whether to buy a stock bull or use artificial insemination (AI) to get them in calf. As only top class bulls should be used and they cost a lot of money, a lot will depend on the size of the herd as to whether the cost of buying a stock bull can be justified or not. If it is only to be a small herd and the breeder has some experience of knowing when cows are in season, then AI may be the best. In this way it will be possible to use semen from the top sires in the breed and select sires to suit individual females.

The one problem is that there are usually one or two cows that are difficult to get in calf and it can cost a lot of money to keep inseminating them with expensive semen. If they do not settle after three tries it may be best to then use a nominated MMB bull to (sweep up), which will be cheaper, with a better chance of getting them in calf as the semen is usually of a higher standard than that of some privately owned bulls.

Avoid using home bred bulls to "sweep up," unless they are of top quality, as it becomes all too easy to serve cows with them rather than to bother with the inseminator, and before you know it, half the herd is in calf to an inferior bull.

Using Stock bulls

The big advantage of using a stock bull is that it can be turned in with the cows in the knowledge that it will not miss any of them when they are in season. The disadvantage is that you are putting all your eggs in one basket and if stock bull turns out "dud" leaving only inferior calves, this will affect you for about three years. The best of both worlds is to have a stock bull but still use a certain percentage of AI until he proves to be a reliable breeder

Calving policies

There are many factors which have to be considered when deciding when to calve the main part of the herd, including what is best with regard to management, selling and showing.

Calving to suit management

If you are working single handed and have nobody you can depend on to see to the calving cows when you are away at major shows or sales, plan nine months ahead and take out the bull from the cows, or stop inseminating for a fortnight. Then you can go away and not have to worry about losing calves.

Calving cows from January to April has the advantage that the calves are nice and strong when turned out to grass in the spring capable of taking full advantage of the new grass, and when they are taken inside for the winter they can be weaned, and housed separate from their mothers. Those born later in the year will be too young to wean and will either have to run with their mothers, or be housed separately and suckled twice a day throughout the winter.

Spring calving heifers are best calved before they are before they go out to grass. This makes it easier to control their protein intake, If they go out on to fresh, high protein grass, the calves they are carrying will grow rapidly and this may lead to calving difficulties.

Calving to suit shows

If you intend to exhibit regularly at summer shows, where most classes start on the first of January, it is best to have a lot of January calves to pick from, as it always an advantage to have one of the oldest ones in the class, especially if you are showing yearlings, where, if they are giving away three months difference in age, they will also be giving away.three months difference in size and as the old saying goes "a good big one, will beat a good little one every time".

Calving to suit sales

If you are going to concentrate on the Autumn sales, April to July is the best time to calve, because this will mean that the bull calves can be sold when they are between 15 and 18 months of age, which is usually the most economic age at which to sell them. Another advantage is at this age they will be sold in the middle of the sale, a period when the prices are often highest.

Culling

The success of any herd depends entirely on the breeder's ability to judge his own cattle and recognise any cattle are not up to standard. Culling females should begin right from the first crop of calves. Any heifers not up to breed standard should go for slaughter as soon as they come to an economic slaughter weight, otherwise if they are sold for breeding they will only go on to produce inferior calves, this will only depress an already saturated market still further. Remember it's "Sod's" law that inferior heifers taken into the herd and bred from, always seem to have heifer calves. In no time at all you can finish up with a herd full of inferior cattle.

The second cull should be heifers that are up to breed standard, but not up to the standard set by the individual breeder. These can be prepared for selling at society sales, with the proceeds going to help cash flow, or buying superior females.

Culling young bulls

It does not pay to cull bull calves too soon. Some bull calves can be very disappointing when they are about four months old, but if they showed promise when they were born, there is every chance that will come again.

Any young bulls that are of the wrong conformation or are bad on their legs, should be sold for killing whenever they come to an economic killing weight, as there is often more profit in a bull that is sold for 1000 gns for killing, than one that is sold for 1500 gns at a major sale, when you subtract the expense of transport, auctioneers on, Hotel bills for the breeder and stockman, etc.

Heat detection & Artificial Insemination

Heat Detection

The average breeding cycle for cattle is 21 days, with the "standing heat" period lasting from 12 to 24 hours, this is referred to by stockmen as "bulling", or, "in season". Heifers come in heat for the first time at about six months of age.

"Standing heat" is the period during estrus when the cow will "stand" and let the bull or other cows jump on her.

Most breeders of pedigree beef cattle, calve their heifers between two and a half and three years of age, Calving heifers under two years of age stunts their development and is not recommended.

Cows should not be served or inseminated until at least six weeks after calving. While there is no doubt the will conceive as early as three weeks after calving, it has been my experience that they may do this a couple of times hard running but will then take "time off" when they next calve and not go back in calf for three or four months.

The most regular breeding cows I have had, were ones that calved every 12 months. Most of them would not come in season until at least 9 weeks after calving but would nearly always go in calf the first time they were served or inseminated.

Many people complain that they have difficulty noticing cows in season. I think a lot of the problem is that they do not know all the signs to look for. For while it is easy to spot cows bulling when there are a couple of them bulling in mid-summer, when the "standing" heat may last for 24 hours; it is not so easy if only one is bulling in the winter, when the "standing" heat may only last for 12 hours.

Another reason why it is sometimes difficult to notice cows bulling, is that because of mineral and trace element deficiencies, they are not coming into a proper heat. Internal examination will reveal very little "tone" in their uterus.

In order not to miss cows that are bulling check them as often as possible, at least three times a day. I find that I spot most of them either first thing in the morning or last thing at night, but it good policy to make a habit of looking out for them at all times.

Signs to look for

The most obvious sign of bulling, is when a cow is trying to jump on the others and they will not stand for her. She will also be extruding clear slime from her vagina and will stand passively if the other cows jump on her.

When two or more cows in the same group are bulling, sometimes others non- bulling ones will join in, It may be necessary to study them for some time in order to determine which ones are "standing". If cows are bulling in adjoining pens, or fields, often they will not try to jump on the others in their group, but will keep pacing up and down the fence trying to get through to the bulling one on the other side.

Always remember, if a cow is trying to jump the others, and they will not "stand" for her, she is the one that is bulling, whereas, if a cow jumps on another one and it stands, it is the one that "stands" that is bulling. The exceptions to this rule, are old in-calf cows with itchy tail heads, who will "stand" to anything that jumps on them just for the pleasure of getting their tailhead scratched. Such cows are often misdiagnosed as bulling and inseminated, causing them to abort.

Cows that have been bulling will have the hair on their tailheads all ruffled, and have mud on their flanks if the fields are wet. Ignore the odd mark on other cows, as these are are due to the bulling one trying to jump on them.

It helps a lot with heat detection if you have a rough idea when to expect cows to come bulling. For this reason it is worth while marking down the dates of any cows seen bulling prior to when they are to be served. Always keep a look out for any signs of menstruation (blood on their tails), this is a sign that they were bulling 24 hours earlier.

Teasers (vasectomised bulls) for heat detection.

Teasers can be very helpful in bringing cows that are bulling to your notice. Young ones are best, because older teasers will very often only serve a cows once then ignore them. Once served cows seem to go off standing heat quicker than they would otherwise.

The one reservation that I have about using teasers is, that if there is any venereal disease in the herd, there is always the risk of the teaser spreading it to the others.

Bull calves - for heat detection

Bull calves become sexually active at an early age and are able to pick out cows that are coming into heat more than 24 hours before they get to the stage where they will stand, While they are too small to reach the cows to serve them, they will however, keep trying, so if cows that are running with bull calves are checked twice a day, there should be very little chance of bulling ones being missed. But remember, while this is a sure way of noticing cows in season, it doesn't do the bull calves much good, as they will not put on much weight if they are continually chasing the bulling cows and trying to serve them.

In-calf cows - for heat detection.

Often in herds where there is no bull present, an old in-calf cow will take over the role of a bull. It will be seen jumping any cow that is bulling, and, like a bull, will chase off any other cows that try to jump the bulling one. Once recognised such cows can be a great asset in heat detection.

Cows running with the bull

It is not always easy to tell when cows that are running with the bull have been served. Apart from actually seeing them served, the most obvious sign is when they walk about with their tails up. Often when old bulls are running with a large number of cows the only sign that a cow is in season is that the bull will "pal up" with her and follow her around. If this is seen, then there is every chance that she will be served as soon as she come into a standing heat.

If more than one bull is being used in the herd it is very important to record the dates when bulls or cows were moved from one group to another. Otherwise there may be problems identifying the sires of the calves, when registering them.

Synchronised heats

Synchronising the heats of animals for inseminating has the advantage that with a bit of luck they can all be inseminated on the same day. Results vary, with some breeders getting good results and doing it on a regular basis, while others say it's a waste of time. One thing to remember is, that if they are all inseminated on the same day, there is every chance that they will all calve on the same day.

Artificial insemination (AI)

Many breeders (especially those of continental cattle) rely entirely on AI to get their cows in calf, with varying degrees of success. The most common cause of poor conception rates is that the cows are not artificially inseminated at the proper time or are wrongly diagnosed as bulling.

Another reason for poor conception rates, especially when using semen from privately owned bulls, is the quality of the semen used. It has been my experience that there is a vast variation in conception rates between different privately owned bull's semen, anywhere from 20% to 90%. Milk Marketing Board semen quality standards are very high, with very good conception rates.

Do it yourself AI (DIY- AI)

DIY-AI has become very popular over the past few years, and is well within the capabilities of the average stockman. Five day courses are available either from the Milk Marketing Board, or private firms. Anyone doing DIY-AI must have a certificate of competence, which is awarded on achieving the set standard at the end of the DIY course. A licence to store semen is also needed, which can be obtained from the Ministry of Agriculture.

DIY-AI has several has advantages, the main one being that inseminating can be done at the time when the cow is most likely to conceive, another, is that as the onus is on the stockman to get good results, he will make sure that the cows are in the right breeding condition, and that any cows showing abnormal vaginal discharges are washed out with the appropriate medication before it is time to inseminate them.

The routine that I have found to be most effective when inseminating is that any animal that comes bulling before midday, is inseminated late that afternoon, while any that come on in the afternoon are inseminated the next morning before nine o'clock.

Bear in mind, that cows will conceive if inseminated up to 12 hours from the end of the standing heat. Animals that fail to conceive to the first service are given an injection of multi vitamins when they next come into season.

Any animal that repeats for the third time is inseminated and given a hormone injection such as 'receptal' to stimulate the ovaries. (consult your vet), then re-inseminated six hours later. The following day she has her cervix washed with a mild solution of iodine to stimulate the womb. When practising DIY-AI, it is absolutely essential to record the insemination as soon as it is carried out. Otherwise it may be forgotten.

Calving

Introduction
There is no such thing as trouble free calving and anyone who tells you that they never lose a calf is either a very good stockman or someone who hasn't calved many cows, but provided a few basic rules are adhered to, losses can be kept to a minimum. I would like to make it clear from the start that calving cows is a skill that can only be learned from experience, and unless you fully understand what you are doing, it is far better to call in the vet if you suspect that something is wrong.

The importance of hygiene when calving, cannot be over-emphasised and the use of disposable plastic gloves for preliminary inspections is highly recommended. All calving ropes, calving aids etc. should be thoroughly washed and disinfected immediately after use and stored somewhere handy so that you don't have to go hunting for them the next time they are needed.

Minerals
Mineral and trace element deficiencies cause more calving problems than is generally realised. In herds where there are difficulties getting cows in calf, or cows do not go into proper labour when calving, it is advisable to take random blood samples from about six

cows, to establish the herd's mineral and trace element status.

Pre-calving diet and Condition.

While there can be no doubt that the condition of cattle prior to calving has an influence on the ease with which they calve, it seems that in general the most important factor is their diet for the last six weeks before calving. Cattle, especially heifers calving for the first time, should be restricted to a diet of hay or second grade silage for the last six weeks of pregnancy. Otherwise if they are fed a lot of high protein feeding, the calf will grow rapidly inside them, resulting in a higher birth weight, and possible calving difficulties.

Housing

Wherever possible cows should be calved inside. This makes it a lot easier to keep an eye on them, and if they are put into batches in order of calving when they are weaned; this gets all the fighting over before they come inside.

Cows should be left in the yard along with their mates right up until they calve, because once they select a place to calve, and are then moved, they will often hang on for hours, and do nothing.

I always like to calve cows in yards that have a good build up of bedding on the floors. Then if the cow has a difficult calving and is weak on her legs, she will be able to get a good grip with her feet when she tries to get up. Cows that cannot get up, recover a lot quicker laying on warm muck, than on a cold concrete floor.

Calving aids - Jacks

Calving aids are essential if you are calving single handed, especially if the animals are of the larger continental breeds: Care and common sense must be used, otherwise there is a chance of damaging both the cow and the calf. Calving aids should only be used after the calving has reached the stage where the calf's feet are showing outside the cow. Any pulling that has to be done before this stage should be done by hand.

The major advantage of using a calving aid is the ability to control the amount of pull, and take up the tension when the cow strains. In this way the calf comes out with one steady pull and seldom gets stuck at the hips.

Always remember that the ratchet handle on a calving-aid is made to a specific length, to predetermine the amount of pressure that can be applied, and _under no circumstances whatsoever_ should it be lengthened by putting a length of pipe, or suchlike over it. Special ropes are available for use with calving-aids, these are spliced to make them wider and flatter, which reduces the chance of damage to the calf's legs when they are being pulled.

Safety

When a cow goes into labour this triggers her mothering instinct to defend the newborn calf and even the quietest old cow in the yard can sometimes turn quite nasty for a day or two after calving, so always treat them with respect. If it is necessary to help a cow to calve, always tie her up. There is nothing worse than helping a cow to calve in the middle of a yard, and the minute she calves, she gets up and faces you, before you have time to get the ropes off the calf and see that it is alright.

Gestation periods

Gestation periods vary slightly between breeds. From my experience Aberdeen Angus calve 9 months and 3 days after service, Beef Shorthorns 9 month and 9 days, and Charolais 9 months and 14 days. There is also a difference between individual sires within a breed of up to ten days. As a rule, the shorter the gestation period the easier they are to calve. The trouble with cows that go a long way past their time is that after 9 months and 20 days you think they are going to calve to another service and relax your vigilance and get caught out with a large calf when you are least expecting it. When calculating calving dates mentally, I find it a lot easier to count three months back, rather than nine months forward.

I never like to induce cows to calve unless I am 100% sure of their service date. Otherwise there is always the chance of aborting a premature calf. Cows that are induced to calve often retain their cleansing which can sometimes cause problems of infection.

Signs of calving

About three weeks before she is due, or earlier, the cow will show a freshness in her udder and start to get flabby around her vagina. this will continue to get more noticeable the nearer she gets to calving.

About three days before calving the ligaments on either side of her tail will start to slacken off, until on the day of calving they will have slackened right off. With a bit of experience it is possible to predict if a cow is going to calve within the next twelve hours.

In my experience,cows that show no signs of calving at ten o'clock at night usually don't calve before five o'clock in the morning, Nevertheless cows that have gone a long way past their calving date often calve at very short notice.

The first sign that a cow has actually starting to calve is when she becomes very alert and keeps turning in circles with her tail up, if she is out in the field she will usually pick a spot away from the main herd and after half an hour she will lie down and have a few contractions then get up and walk about for a minute or two then lie down and have a few more.

Eventually, but not always (it sometimes bursts inside) the first water bag (referred to by stockmen as the first water) containing a very watery fluid will appear and burst. This will be followed a little later by a second water bag containing a much thicker liquid which is referred to by stockmen as the feet water, because very often the feet will be seen in the bag before it bursts. During this time the cow will keep lying down and getting up until the calf is born,

Immediately the calf is born the cow will "hopefully" get up on her feet and start licking it and pushing it about with her nose to try and get it breathing. Some cows get very excited at this stage and will give the impression that they are trying to kill their calves, but if left alone, they usually settle down when the calf gets on its feet. I have never known a cow to damage her calf in this way.

Because of the value of pedigree animals and the amount of time and effort put into trying to breed good ones, I always try to see every cow calve, just in case the calf is born with the water bag still over its face and the cow through exhaustion or laziness fails to get up and lick it off.

Deciding when to help
It is very difficult to tell anyone when a cow needs to be helped. As

a rule if she is not getting on with calving within a couple of hours of when she first went into labour, she should be examined carefully to see if the calf is in the right position. If it is, then she should be left to get on with it, and no further help given until the feet and nose are showing, unless she goes a further two hours without progressing. or shows signs of severe distress,

There are only two positions in which a calf can be calved. Either position **(A)** the normal position where two front feet are being presented (with the dew claws facing downwards) and the head above them. Or position **(B)** where two hind feet are being presented with the dew claws facing upwards.

Correct normal presentation position of calf for calving. Diagram (A).

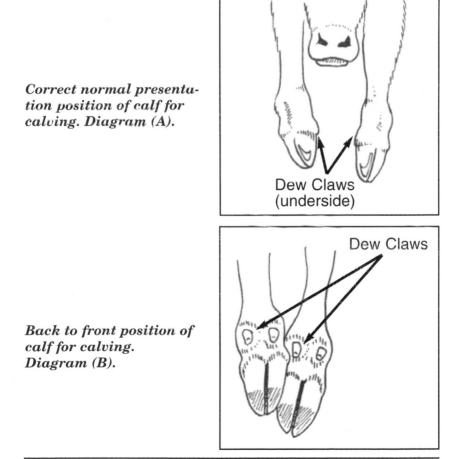

**Dew Claws
(underside)**

Dew Claws

Back to front position of calf for calving. Diagram (B).

Check before pulling

Before any ropes are put on the calf, it must be established that the calf is being presented in the correct position. If on examination you can find two feet but no sign of a head, don't take it for granted that they are back feet. Reach in and check the knee joints. There is absolutely no way that front legs can be mistaken for hind legs, or vice versa, and if you can't tell the difference, leave the animal alone, and call the vet.

Pulling the calf

The calf should only be pulled if it is absolutely necessary, as I am sure that more calves are lost through being pulled too soon, than by being left alone. If it has to be done wait until the calf's feet are showing, then after tying up the cow, put the calving ropes on the calf's legs above the dew claws, attach the calving-aid, and with the handle pointing towards the floor, start moving the ratchet handle back and forward. When the calf's head comes out, speed up the action, so that there is no slack which would let the aid slip out of place. Keep the ratchet going right up until the calf is completely out.

When you are calving a cow that is lying down, always have the ratchet bar of the calving-aid as far round towards the cow's back feet as possible. Take care that your clothing does not get caught up in the ratchet, as it can be very difficult to get it free again.

If the calf gets stuck at the hips, stop pulling, clean any mucus that's around its mouth and nose, and try to get it to start breathing before starting to pull again. At this stage it is best to pull only for short spells, giving it a rest in between. Sustained pressure will cause severe stress and make it difficult for the calf to breathe, with less chance of it surviving.

Often, when a calf is stuck at the hips, if you manage to rotate it a little bit, it will pop out almost on its own. The most important thing to remember when a calf gets stuck at the hips, is, not to panic. I have on more than one occasion managed to calve a live calf after it had been stuck at the hips for 45 minutes.

Any calf that does not look too bright when it is born should be picked up by its heels and give it a shake. Then put it lying on its chest with its front legs on either side of it and put a bit of baler twine or straw up its nose to try to get it to shake its head. If it does it's usually alright, but if not, throw half a bucket of cold water over its head (only do this once) in the hope that this will make it gasp and get some air into its lungs.

If the calf still does not respond and start breathing, stand astride it and put a hand under each side of its chest and lift it up and down, pressing on its ribs at the same time at about the same speed as it would breathe. As long as there is a heartbeat keep going. It may take 15 minutes or more but it's worth it to get a live calf.

Calves coming in the wrong position
Back to front
A lot of people, on finding that a calf is coming back to front, will try to calve it long before the cow has opened up. They fear that the calf will drown, but as the calf will not start breathing until the navel cord is broken, or severely restricted (and this will not happen until the calf is half way out) there is no need to panic. I have in fact on two occasions calved live calves from cows where the hind feet have been showing for more than six hours.

Before you start pulling make sure it is two hind feet you have, and once the hips come out try to keep the calf coming out in one steady pull. This is where a calving-aid really comes into its own.

Back to front and upside down
Calves in this position are very misleading, because on first examination the feet will be found with the dew claws facing downwards, giving them every appearance of front feet. It is only when you can't find the head, that you become aware that there is a problem. Turning the calf is a matter of luck.

Sometimes they will turn with no trouble at all, and other times they will drive you to despair. I have always had more success turning calves clockwise, and if the feet can be rotated with one hand while the palm of the other hand can reach under the hip and push it up, often the calf will float round without too much trouble. Once turned I then like to get the calf out straight away in case the navel cord is wrapped around it and restricted.

Legs back

When front or hind legs are back, care must be taken not to damage the womb. First push the calf back as far as you can, then try to get the palm of your hand under the calf's foot before pulling it forward. This way there is less chance of doing any damage.

Dead calves

Sometimes calves (especially twins) will die in the womb about 2 or 3 days before they are due to be born> This causes the womb to become very fragile, so great care has to be taken when helping them to calve. Any bruising or tearing will soon lead to peritonitis.

Heads back

Calves with their heads back are usually the hardest to get into position, mainly because of the difficulty in reaching in far enough to get hold of the jaw to get the head turned forward. In most cases a rope will be needed to keep the head in place. This is best done by putting a surgical hook in the calf's furthest away eye socket (leave this to the vet and don't worry it won't damage the eye). Sometimes it is possible to put a loop of rope around the back of the calf's head and through its mouth. This is not easy to do, especially with big calves, inside deep cows.

Once the head is in the right position any pulling should be done on the legs, with only enough strain on the rope on the calf's head to keep it in position. While it is alright to pull a calf's bottom jaw with your hand, never pull on the jaw with a rope, in case you damage it.

Twins

It is not always possible to tell whether a cow is going to have twins, simply by the size of her abdomen. If a cow calves a calf that is smaller than you were expecting, it pays to keep an eye on her in case she has another one.

Twins, because they are usually smaller, should not cause too many problems so long as you stick to the golden rule of never pulling before you are sure that you have two front feet and a head, or two back feet and a tail, and that both feet belong to the same calf.

Caesarean

As a rule, if the cow can get the calf to the stage where the front feet and nose, or the back feet and knee joints are showing, with a bit of luck and a calving-aid you should be able to calve it. The time to think about doing a caesarean is when a cow or heifer has been trying hard to calve for some time with no progress and when you attempt to calve her you are unable to get any "give" when trying to pull one foot out past the other.

Remember it's no use after trying for hours to turn, or pull a calf and failed, to ring the vet to do a caesarean and expect him to produce a live calf. No matter how good he is at caesarean operations, if the calf is dead before he starts the operation, it will still be dead when he has finished.

One point I should mention here is, that unless the cows or heifers that are caesared are far enough into labour to trigger their mothering instinct, they will very often reject their calves.

Prejudice against caesarean operations

Many breeders (especially of native breeds) have told me that they have never, and would never, do a caesarean on any of their animals. When asked how many calves they lost, or how many cows had to be put down because of bad calvings, they did admit to having a few.

The point I am trying to make, is, that no matter how skilled you are at calving, sooner or later there will come a time when, due to a calf being in such a position that it cannot be turned, or simply being too big, it can't be calved. It is my firm belief that on such an occasion, it is far better to admit defeat and make arrangements to get a caesarean done while the calf is still living, than to persevere and lose both the calf and the cow.

Especially when a vet who has experience of doing caesars, can have the calf out within 20 minutes of arriving at the farm, with every chance of it being alive; very little stress to the cow; and every chance of the animal going back in calf without any trouble.

Care of the calf immediately after calving
Make sure the calf sucks

It is very important that the calf sucks within 6 hours of birth, as after this it is unable to absorb the antibodies from the colostrum (the enriched milk produced by a cow for a day or two after calving) into its own blood system and is then more likely to suffer from life-threatening infections.

In cases where calves are unable to suck they should be given colostrum straight into their stomach by means of a tube. It is worth remembering that colostrum can be frozen and it is good practice to have some stored in the freezer in case of emergencies.

Most calves that are born without help will be up on their feet and sucking within an hour of birth. The only attention they need then is to have their navel sprayed with iodine or disinfectant to stop any infection getting in.

If the mother has large "windy" teats it may be necessary to help the calf to get the teat in its mouth. This is also necessary when (due to a difficult birth) the calf has a swollen tongue. Remember just because you have seen a calf nosing around its mother's udder this does mean it has sucked. Calves that have never sucked seldom "bawl" with hunger, this only seems to happen after they have had a feed or two. The longer calves go without sucking the harder it is to get them started. Once they go past 12 hours they don't seem to try at all.

Fostering calves

Cows that have had a dead calf will often accept a foster one straight away, provided that it is given to them immediately after they calve, and that it is smeared with the mucus from the dead one. If the calf to be fostered is very big it will need to be either tied up to a rail, or hobbled, so that it does not run away when the cow tries to lick it clean.

While I hate losing calves at birth, I don't feel quite so bad about it if I can get the cow to accept another one, such as a twin, or a good calf from a heifer that is a bad milker. It always seems such a waste for a good milking cow to be idle for a whole year.

Care of the cow after a difficult calving

All cows that have had a difficult calving should be given an injection of long acting penicillin. Followed by a second dose a couple of days later, to prevent infection.

Sometimes when a cow has had a very difficult calving she will have difficulty getting up on her feet straight away, especially if the calf has been stuck at the hips for any length of time. When the usual methods of getting a new calved cow up on her feet, such as putting the calf in front of her, or shouting loudly in her ear fail, it may be best to let her lie. Care should also be taken if the calf is left beside her, in case she tries to get up and staggers on top of it. It pays therefore to put a gate between them until such time as she gets up and gets a bit steadier on her feet. It is very important to leave the calf where she can see it, because not only does it give her an incentive to get up, but there is also less chance of her rejecting it.

Downer cows

Any cows that are not on their feet within 24 hours of calving should be seen by a vet, as medication may help with their recovery.

Cows that have had a difficult calving and are unable to get up sometimes take a long time to recover. They should not be forced to try and get up as this will often do more harm than good. They will come to no harm lying down, provided they are turned over two or three times a day and watch is kept that they don't get bed-sores.

If they are lying in the open they should be covered to keep them warm and help their circulation. Sometimes injections of the cortisone type are beneficial, be guided on this by your vet.

When the cow starts to make a reasonable attempt at getting up she can be given a help. If she does manage to get on her feet, stand beside her and give some support to help her get her confidence back. I have heard of cases where a cows have got back on their feet after having lain for more three weeks. Unless they are turned regularly they will nearly always develop sores and have to be put down.

Two people can usually turn a large cow over from one side to the other. The easiest way is to put a rope on her lower hind leg, and a halter on her head. Then the person pulling the head rope stands at her back and pulls her head round onto her shoulder, The one on the foot rope stands at her back as well and pulls her foot forward. Then with a decent pull she should roll right over her back onto her other side.

I never like to see large cows being lifted on hoists to help them get on their feet, as it always seems to cause them a lot of distress. There may however be circumstances where either air bags or hoists may be used to take the weight off the animal's legs and help circulation.

Post calving diet

It has been my experience that newly calved cows and heifers are best kept on a restricted diet for a day or two after calving to lessen the amount nature (swelling) in their udders making it easier for the calves to suck the teats.

About a week after calving the newly calved cows can given some feeding. The amount can be increased gradually, according to their condition and milking abilities.

Heifers because they are still not fully developed need to be well fed after calving. Not only to to enable them to continue their own development, but that of their calf as well.

Tattooing & dehorning

Tattooing

Most breed societies have a rule that all calves registered have to be tattooed within a month of birth, No anaesthetic is necessary.

As the tattoo will be the breed society's means of identifying the animal for the rest of its life, it is essential that it is done properly so that the tattoo can be easily read when it has to be checked at pre-sale inspections, or herd tests.

Most breed societies have a system whereby each breeder is given an individual herd prefix identification number consisting of three letters. This is tattooed into the ear, along with a letter to represent the year in which the animal was born and a number corresponding to the sequence in which it was born.

Because a young calf's ear is usually not big enough to take all the tattoo if it is put in a single row, it is best to use two rows with the herd prefix in the top row and the year number and sequence num-

Example of a good accept-able tattoo.

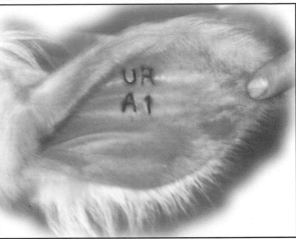

A poor tattoo example.

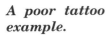

ber below it. The tattoo is inserted in the ear by means of tattooing pliers, preferably a set that does both rows at the same time.

Tattooing should be done when the calf is about 2 weeks old, as by this time its ear will be sufficiently developed. Anyone tattooing calves for the first time, should tattoo one or two crossbreds, before attempting purebreds. Check the tattoo on a piece of paper to make sure it is correct before tattooing the calf's ear. Then having made sure that the calf is tied up tightly so that it does not struggle and cause smudges, rub some tattooing paste into the ear, insert the tattoo, and rub in some more paste.

Make a point of checking all tattoos at a later date to make sure that they are clear and correct. If any mistakes are found, notify the breed society concerned to get their permission to re-tattoo in the other ear. If plastic tags are used for identification purposes, they should be put in the opposite ear to the tattoo, in case they are torn out and damage the tattoo.

Dehorning

Regulations (at the time of writing) state that dehorning can only be done by a vet, or by a breeder or stockman with the necessary qualifications, and that no animal can be de-horned without first being given a local anaesthetic.

Dehorning is done by removing the horn buds with either a caustic paste or a gas or electric dehorner. Best results are obtained if the calves are done when they are about two weeks old. Dehorning should only be done by vets or qualified stockmen so I will not go into further detail on this subject as you will need to go on a training course before doing it yourself.

Feeding & weight recording

Feeding

When stockmen talk about animals being "fed" or "given feeding", this refers to concentrates or special cereal mixtures, given to animals in addition to what they are given for maintainence.

Maintenance is the basic feeds such as silage beet pulp, hay, etc. given to cattle in order for them to maintain their condition.

Creep feeders, are hoppers that are specially designed with an entrance that is low enough to keep out the cows, but high enough for the calves to creep under to get to the feeding.

Feeding Calves

It is essential that young calves get a good start in life and they should encouraged to eat from an early age. Protein content for young calves should be somewhere between 16% and 18%. Depending on their condition this will need to be cut back to 14% as they get older. Otherwise they will put on more weight than their underdeveloped bone structure can carry, resulting in twisted legs and bad feet.

Feeding Yearling Bulls

Over the years I have studied how some of the more successful stockmen feed their animals, and because their methods vary so much, I have come to the conclusion that there are no hard and fast rules, other than ensuring that the food is palatable with the right amount of protein and that feeding times are regular.

The traditional way of feeding bulls from native breeds, was to give them two dry feeds and two wet feeds per day. The dry feed would consist of a mixture of rolled oats, flaked maize, linseed cake, locust beans and fish meal, which would be fed first thing in the morning and again in mid-afternoon, while the wet feed consisting of rolled oats, bran, beet pulp, barley and malt extract, would be mixed with boiling water and allowed to stand for a couple of hours before being fed at mid-day, and again in the evening.

With the introduction of continental cattle into this country, many of the breeders who had never fed bulls before, fed them the same way that they would their fat bullocks. They gave them only dry feeding but still got excellent results. This led to a change in the methods of feeding, and while some stockmen still feed four times a day and give the animals only as much feed as they will clear up within half an hour of being fed, others only feed twice a day and give them as much as they will clear up before it is time for their next feed.

Because of the very high cost of traditional feeding stuffs such as bran, flaked maize, and flaked barley, many breeders are turning to pre-mixed feeds which can be bought either as pellets or meal. These consist of by-products, such as biscuit meal, maize gluten, citrus pulp, corn flakes and pasta, with the protein coming from oil seed rape pulp, and fish meal. These feeds can give very good results, especially if they have some wet sugar beet pulp mixed in to make them more palatable. Avoid feeding too much low protein; high fibre; roughage as this will make young bulls too "gutty."

Old bulls

Old bulls that are to be shown or are working hard, should be given the same mixture as the young bulls. Otherwise in order that they don't get too fat they should be given a maintenance diet.

Yearling and two year old heifers

In order to ensure that yearling and two year old heifers get every chance develop to their full potential, they should be given enough feeding to maintain a steady live weight gain, But take care not to get them too fat.

Dry cows

Dry cows should be kept on a maintainence diet.

Cows in milk

Newly calved cows should be fed according to their condition and milking abilities, to maintain a rising plane of condition for the first three months.

When their calves get to the stage that they are eating a fair amount of feeding, the amount of feed given to their mothers can be reduced.

Weight Recording

The Meat and Livestock commission provides a service whereby they weigh young cattle within a herd every 100 days. Weights are then calculated to give figures for their weight at 100, 200, 300 and 400 days

Average weights at 100, 200, 300 and 400 days for the main breeds are included in the chapter headed "Breed societies" at the end of this book. But these are averages, to be successful your herd needs to be above average, while at the same time you should remember that young stock should be fed according to how much the their legs will stand, not by how much they should weigh at a certain age. It's no use having an animal 40% above breed at 400 days average if it can't walk properly.

Chapter two

Seasonal work

January

Having recovered from the Christmas festivities, it's back to work in earnest. The first of the new season's calves will be starting to appear, along with a few frozen pipes, and all the other little things that are sent to try you, when you are busy enough already, trying to put the finishing touches to the bulls entered for the spring sales, which for most breeds are held in the first week in February.

The bulls being sold will need to have their feet and hair trimmed, and be tied up, groomed, and led out on a halter every day to get them used to being handled. They will also need to be washed at least once a week if they are sweating a lot, and have their hair blown once or twice, to get them used to blowers, and be trained with a show stick, how to stand with their feet in the correct position

It also pays to do a pre sale check that their teeth and testicles are o.k; that they are free of lice; mange and warts; that their tattoos are still legible and correspond with the ones entered in the sale catalogue.

If the bulls are housed in small individual bull boxes, they will need to be exercised daily to keep their legs and feet right. This is not quite so essential when the bulls are run together in groups, as they move about the pens a lot more.

Keep a close watch on the young calves, and if they show any signs of scour, pneumonia, or swollen navels, treat them straight away, and watch that there are no young calves lying in front of the troughs when you give the cows their feeding, or they may get trampled on.

Don't forget that most breed societies require all calves to be tattooed and registered within a month of birth, and that calves that have to be dehorned should be done when they are about two weeks old.

Take advantage of any hard frost, to muck out any yards where the muck has got too deep.

February

If you have bulls entered for the February sales, the first two weeks of the month can be very hectic, If you have a good trade and manage to sell all the animals you entered, you will come home feeling good, and raring to get your summer show team picked out penned up and get started on them.

On the other hand if you have had a bad trade, there is likely be an inquest to find out where you went wrong, and how to improve things for next time. This is not always easy to do, because if the reason for your bad sale was that your stock bull is leaving calves of the wrong type, and all your cows are in calf to him again, you will have another two crops of calves by him to sell before you have bulls old enough to sell by his successor. This is why it is best not to put all your cows in calf to the same bull until he has proved himself.

Depending on how many bulls were sold (if any) there will be a few empty pens which can be used for the summer show cattle or to divide up some of the young stock that have become overcrowded.

Calves born April, May, June the previous year should be weaned now to let their mothers get a rest before calving again.

Make sure the minerals you are feeding at this time of year are high in magnesium to lessen the chances of cattle going down with hypomagnescemia (staggers) when they are turned out to grass.

Any spare time available should spent trimming cows' feet, or halter breaking young stock before they go out to the grass for the summer. Put rings in the noses of any young bulls that are weaned.

March

Carry on with the foot trimming and halter breaking, also check and, if necessary, repair all fences, clean out the water troughs and have the fields ready for when the cattle are turned out.

If you intend to start calving at the beginning of January you will need to put the bulls in with the cows, or start inseminating about the middle of the month; any earlier and there is a chance that they will calve in December.

Try to find time to groom the show cattle every day, in order to get all the old winter coat out, and get them used to being handled. If they are washed at least once a week it will help a fresh coat to come in.

Any heifers that are to be shown should be trained to lead with a "bulldog" in their nose, as this makes it a lot easier to control them.

April
Depending on how handy the paddocks are to the cattle sheds, start running the cows with calves out all day, then in again at night to get them hardened off ready for when the weather is suitable for them to go out all night, this also reduces the risk of hypo-mag-nescemia in the cows.

Make a habit of putting a little bit of feeding in the trough ready for them to eat when they come in, because if you can teach them to come in when they are called, it is a lot easier than having to chase them. Keep feeding them hay or silage so that the changeover to grass is not too sudden.

Depending on weather conditions, and what part of the country you are in, it may be possible to turn out the dry cows and two-year-old heifers all night by the end of the month. Any empty pens should be mucked out, and either steam cleaned, or pressure washed and disin-fected, the first chance you get. Otherwise if they are not done before the rush starts with showing and hay making, there is a fair chance that they won't be done until they are needed again in the Autumn.

May
By now most of the cattle will be outside all the time except for the ones that are going to be shown and any young bulls that you intend to sell at the autumn sales. In order to keep these right on their legs they will need to run out for a while in a paddock every day, and if you have a lot of groups it may be necessary to put some of them out all night and the others out all day.

Wherever possible the cattle in the fields should be checked and counted twice a day. The importance of counting them is that if an animal is ill, or calving, it will very often be on its own out of sight and will otherwise not be missed.

Another reason for checking twice a day is that if a cow goes down with hypomagnescemia soon after you checked them in the morning, she will almost certainly be dead if not treated before the following morning.

Start routine worming this month. Be advised by the manufacturers recommendations.

Try and get all the yards mucked out, pressure washed, and disinfected before starting the hay and silage, as this will go a long way towards eliminating diseases.

The show season really gets underway this month, and if you are doing a lot of shows, make sure that the cattle at home are not being neglected. If, for instance, you put off inseminating cows because you are going to be away at a show, saying that they can be done next time, and this happens once or twice, its surprising how much time can be lost getting them in calf.

June

The January-born heifer calves will be getting nearly old enough to start coming in season, and should be separated from the bull calves, for while the bull calves may not be able to serve them, they will soon lose a lot of weight if they are riding and fighting all day.

Old bulls should also be kept separate from any heifers over six months of age, for while you might think that it is not possible for a heifer to carry the weight of an old bull to get served, they nearly always manage to, somehow.

If an under age heifer gets served, leave her for three weeks to see if she comes bulling again, if not, get the vet to give her an injection to terminate the pregnancy.

Now that the first flush of grass is past, its time to start creep feeding the older calves, if you have not already done so. There will be a lot of flies about by this time of year and you will need to keep a close watch out for summer mastitis in the dry cows, especially if you are in a problem area. Any animal affected should be treated straight away.

It is also very important to check the navels of any new born calves that are out in the fields for any sign of infection, which, if not treated straight away will often cause joint ill.

This month sees the first of the major shows, the Royal Highland at Edinburgh, and also the start of hay making. At busy times like this it's all to easy to concentrate too much on the hay, and skimp on the cattle. It's a pity to lose a calf which may have been worth thousands of pounds (through being too busy to make sure it was alright when it is born) while trying to get in a some bales of hay worth a few hundreds.

This is why it is often best to have any cows that are due to calve inside, as this makes it a lot easier to keep an eye on them. When you are busy you can do without having to go down the field to check them, or the hassle of having to take them in if they are needing help.

The older calves should be starting to take a fair amount of feeding now and beginning to fill out. Hopefully all the cows that are running with the bull calves are in calf now, otherwise the bull calves will be getting themselves sweated up riding them every time they come bulling. It wouldn't be so bad if it was just for a day but they usually start chasing the cows the day before they come in season.

July

There is always a mad scramble to get the last of the hay in before going to The Royal Show which takes place in the first full week of this month. If you are exhibiting, remember that all cattle are checked by vets at the entrance gate. Any showing signs of infectious skin diseases such as ringworm or mange will not be admitted.

If it has been a very dry spell the grass will be starting to burn up, so make sure the calves are getting enough creep feed. Also remember to worm the calves if necessary.

The oldest bull calves will be getting too big to get into the creep now and it is often best to feed them inside. If the bull calves are taken in twice a day, and separated from their mothers and put in the other half of the yard, they can then be fed on their own. Leave them in for a couple of hours to eat up their feed, then chase them back out along with their mothers. One advantage of feeding them this way, is that the greedy ones don't get a chance to stand in the creep guzzling feed all day and getting too fit too soon.

The easiest way to separate the bull calves from their mothers is to put some feeding in the trough for the mothers, and while they are eating it, slip the bull calves into the other half of the yard. It usually only takes them a couple of days to get into the routine.

Towards the end of the month most of the shows will be past. and the show animals should be turned out to grass. including any bulls or heifers that you intend to carry on and sell at the Autumn sales. for unless they get a break from feeding for a month or so they usually go very stale. Now's the time to try and get a day or two's holiday before the harvest starts.

August
Back to work after the holidays, and it's time fill up the pens vacated by the show team with the bulls entered for the Autumn sales. Remember to check their teeth, tattoos, and testicles to make sure they are OK. It's better to find any faults now, rather than at the pre-sale inspection.

In order get good coats of hair on them for the sale, they should be washed at least once a week, and run out in a paddock all night.

If young bulls are running in groups, try not to move animals from one group to another, as this will lead to fighting. If serious fighting occurs within a group it may be necessary to take out the "trouble maker", and put him in a pen on his own. _Never_ go into a pen among a batch of young bulls to try and stop a fight, you will only end up getting hurt.

If you have been taking the oldest bull calves in twice a day to feed, they will have settled into the routine by now. If you want to start handling them, keep them in all day, then let them back out with their mothers after they have had their afternoon feed, or they can be kept separate from their mothers and suckled twice a day.

Problems like summer mastitis and pink eye will be at their peak this month and must be treated straight away to save any unnecessary suffering.

September
If there has been a lot of rain and the gateways are muddy, you will most probably get animals going lame with "foul of the foot" from now till the end of the year.

October
Most of the time this month will need to be spent putting the finishing touches on any bulls that are going to the Autumn sales. Remember to do a final pre sale check of teeth and testicles; that they are free of lice. mange and warts and that their tattoos are legible and correspond with the ones in the sale catalogue.

November
Having got rid of one lot of bulls, it's time to fill up the pens with bulls entered for the Spring sales. Don't forget to check their tattoos, teeth and testicles.

It will be starting to get a bit chilly at night now and its time for the calves to be taken inside for the winter. Those born from January to the end of March can be weaned. The calves born from April to August will be too young to wean and will either have to run with their mothers, or preferably be penned separately and let in with their mothers to suckle twice a day. When weaned, the cows that had bull calves and the ones that had heifer calves can be put together in one group. They will be too busy bawling for their calves to think about fighting.

The later calves are left out, the hairier they get, which in turn will make them more susceptible to pneumonia when they are taken inside for the winter because they will sweat a lot. Wherever possible, newly weaned calves should be housed in open fronted pens to reduce the risk of pneumonia. If they are in pens with poor ventilation, it will pay to clip the hair from under their bellies, and a strip along their backs, to help stop them sweating. When you take the dry cows in all night, pen them up into groups in the order that they will be calving, as any movement of cattle between groups later on, will lead to fighting.

December

Routine work will take up most of the time. Make sure that all cattle are well bedded, especially the cows with calves, for if they get their teats dirty, their calves won't suck them, leading to all kinds of problems. I've often heard it said that a good bed is worth half a feed.

Towards the end of the month preparations will need to be made to make the work load easier over the Christmas period, when staff will be on holiday.

Shows & sales

If you intend to exhibit animals at shows, you will first need to get entry forms from the shows concerned, fill them in and return them before the date specified. While some small shows may accept late entries, major shows are often over-subscribed and stick rigidly to their closing dates for entries, which are usually about three months before the actual show.

Each major breed is judged in its own separate section. The animals are divided into classes according to their age and sex. A typical county show would have separate classes for senior bulls, junior bulls, senior cows, two-year-old heifers, and yearling heifers. At major shows there may be additional classes for two-year-old bulls, and three-year-old cows, and the other classes may be subdivided depending on the number of entries.

Animals in each class are always listed in chronological order to give the judge an idea of how they compare for size against one another.

One day shows

One day shows are usually very enjoyable local events. Judging does not usually start before eleven o'clock in the morning, enabling exhibitors to bring their animals on the morning of the show, although it does usually mean a very early start.

County shows

County shows are usually held over two or three days. The animals arrive the day before the show opens. Standards at these shows are usually very high with some exhibitors travelling long distances to compete. Individual breed classes, championships and groups of three, are usually judged on the first day, followed by Interbreed championships and Interbreed groups on the second day. There is usually a parade of prize winners in the grand ring each day.

Major shows

Major shows such as the Royal Highland, Royal Agricultural Show of England and the Royal Welsh Show, are held over four days. All cattle have to arrive before a specified time, usually midnight on the day prior to the show opening.

Exhibitors who have to travel long distances to major shows usually bring their cattle to the show two or three days before it opens, in order to give them a chance to fill out and look their best for judging day. Cattle that arrive after the specified time are not allowed entry to the show, unless they have a genuine reason, and the show has been notified.

Because of the large number of cattle being exhibited at major shows, judging of the individual breeds is usually done over the first two days, followed by Interbreed groups on the third day, and the supreme individual championship on the last day.

Many breed societies and young farmers' organisations are affiliated to major shows and hold the finals of their stock-judging competitions at them. Exhibitors are required to make their animals available for these events, if requested. Animals involved are usually ones that were not awarded prizes in their class when their breed was judged.

Accommodation

There was a time when only stockmen went to shows with the cattle and they slept in cubicles provided by the show or in the back of their lorries. Living in the back of a lorry for four or five days is not so primitive as one might suppose. Stockmen who exhibit at a number of summer shows, usually fit out their lorries with home comforts. Having washed out the lorry they then put a piece of old carpet on the floor; set up their camp beds and cookers and dine well. Nowadays while some exhibitors sleep in cubicles or the back of their lorries, many now take a caravan to the show and bring their family with them.

Sales

Procedures for entering sales is similar to that for shows. Here again the larger sales stick rigidly to their closing dates for entries. At major multi breed sales venues like Perth, most cattle arrive by the Saturday previous to the sale. During the following week each breed will be inspected, shown and sold. Starting with the Aberdeen Angus followed in turn by the Beef Shorthorn, Limousin, Simmental and Charolais

Accommodation

Most stockmen either stay in hotel or bed and breakfast accommodation during the period of the sale. This has to be booked well in advance because of demand.

Preparation of animals for shows & sales.

Selecting show animals

When selecting animals for shows, always bear in mind that any apparent faults such as bad legs, fatty patches around tailheads, or large briskets, will only get worse when the animal gets heavier and fatter as the season goes on. Always try to pick animals that are sound on their feet, and clean fleshed, as you will then be able to "push them on" through the show season, without worrying about them going "over the top".

Animals that are to be shown should be of good temperament, if you have any doubts about being able to control them it's far better to leave them at home, than have them run away from you at a show and hurt someone.

Most experienced stockmen will recognise potential show animals while they are only young calves. They will keep an eye on them to make sure that they get every chance to develop to their full potential, while at the same time not allow them to get to the stage where they are "fit" for showing too early in the season.

Because of variation in the ability of some animals to put on flesh quicker than others, how much feeding they will need to be given, and when to start feeding, to get them into show condition, can only be learned through experience, so the following is only a rough guide.

Adult cows

Adult cows that are going to be shown with calves at foot are best penned up on their own from about the November prior to the show. They can then be brought on steadily without getting bullied and knocked about. Once calved they can usually be fed fairly hard without coming to any harm.

Two-year-old heifers

Two year old heifers are the easiest to get into show condition, but beware of get them too "fit" too early. Once they go "over the top" and start getting patches of fat around the tailhead, and get too much fat on their brisket, causing them to walk wide on their front legs, there is not much that can be done to remedy the situation.

Yearling heifers

Yearling heifers need to be penned up by the February of the year they are going to be shown. While there is less chance of them going "over the top" than two-year-olds, it is always better to have them under rather than over "fit", especially if you intend to show them again as two-year-olds the next year.

Yearling bulls

Yearling bulls often feed better in groups, and so long as there is not too much fighting among them, they don't need to be penned up individually until a couple of months before the first show. Remember that once a bull is taken out of the group for more than a week, it is very difficult to get it back into the group without a lot of fighting. So in most cases, once the summer shows are finished, its best to keep the bulls that have been shown separate from the others until they are sold.

Adult bulls

Adult bulls need to be carrying a lot of flesh if they are to win major honours at shows. They will need to be started on in good time, and if they are going to have to serve cows right up to, and between shows, it is always best to limit them to one service per cow, otherwise they can soon lose a lot of condition if they are chasing about jumping cows all the time.

The routine I have used for bringing out summer show cattle for the last forty-five years with reasonable success, is as follows. Cattle selected for shows are penned up individually or in pairs whenever pens become available in the spring, (usually the pens that were vacated by the bulls that were sold at the February bull sales). They are fed three times a day with a mixture containing equal parts by weight, of 20% protein dairy meal, and barley, at 7am,12 noon, and at 4pm. They also get a bite of hay or silage after their morning and afternoon feeds.

Whenever the paddocks are dry enough in the spring, the show cattle are turned out for a couple of hours every day for exercise. Then as soon as weather conditions allow, the routine is changed to them being fed at 7am, turned out in the paddock after breakfast, taken back in and fed about 3pm, then given a bite of hay at nine o'clock at night.

Before being turning out after breakfast, they are all tied up and groomed. Then each one is led round the paddock on its own to get it used to being led on the halter, and to being alone. It is stopped every now and again and trained to stand with it's feet in the correct position.

This is repeated daily until such time as the cattle can "hopefully" be relied on to behave themselves in the show ring. While it would be nice to do this routine every day throughout the show season, pressure of work does not often allow it. Every attempt is made to wash them at least once week, preferably on a Friday, so that they are half tidy if any visitors arrive at the weekend and want to see them.

The day prior to them being transported to the show, they are fed as usual in the morning, then their diet is restricted to hay and water, in order to get their dung firm. This makes it easier to keep them clean for judging and parades.

On arrival at the show the cattle are washed and double-tied in their stalls with the halter on one side and a neck rope on the other. Care is taken that any heifers that are expected to come bulling at the show are not standing next to bulls in case they get served, also that any bulls that are being shown are not standing next to those of other exhibitors in case they start fighting. Care is also taken to ensure that any baby calves that are being shown with their mothers, are tied where there is least chance of them getting trampled or lain on.

Having been washed and tied up, they are then given a bite of hay and the offer of a drink of water, then left to settle down, before being given a feed of meal and some more water and hay later in the evening.

On the morning of the judging an early start is necessary, so that any animals that are dirty and have to be washed, will have time to dry before it's time to start dressing them up for judging. It also allows the animals time to chew their cud and fill out after they have been fed, so that they will be looking at their best when they are judged. Cows that are being shown with calf at foot are suckled early in the morning, then the calves are tied up fairly light so that they can't suck again before judging, this gives the cow's udder a chance to fill out enhancing her appearance.

When the animals have all lain down it's time for a quick breakfast and a change of clothes, then back to the cattle before they start getting up, dunging and lying down again in it. They are left to lie, chew their cud and fill out, right up until it's time to start dressing them up for judging. During this time the show halters that are going to be put on them for judging are sorted out, along with the catalogue numbers that have to be tied round their necks. A check is made to make sure that the white coats that must be worn for judging and parades, and judging sticks, have not been left in the lorry or caravan which may be some distance from the cattle sheds.

Preparation for the judging varies with different breeds. Aberdeen Angus and Galloways will have their coats smoothed down with oil, and have their feet blackened, and they will be shown in either a white cotton halter or a black leather one. Horned breeds will have their horns and feet oiled, and are usually shown in brown leather halters, and depending on how much they have, their hair will either have it smoothed down with oil, or rubbed with saddle soap and combed up. Charolais have their hair soaped up with white soap. It pays to try and keep them on their feet, from when they are soaped up until they are judged, otherwise the straw and dust will stick to them.

After judging, animals that have been soaped up are washed to get the soap out of them, otherwise they will look rather grubby by the end of the day with all the straw and dust sticking to them.

The best way to learn how to prepare animals for the show ring, is to offer to help an experienced breeder or stockman at shows or sales. Even though they only ask to shift muck or hold animals at the ringside you will at least get an idea of how to go about the job.

N.B. Too much grass is inclined to make show cattle and young bulls that are being fed for sales, very "gutty" and soft fleshed. For this reason the paddocks that the show cattle and bulls are turned out on, are kept bare of grass, either by reducing the amount of fertiliser, or stocking them with a large number of cattle for a couple of days.

Judging & stewarding

Judging

The most important thing to remember when judging, is to go about it in a professional manner, so that the exhibitors in the ring, and the spectators at the ringside can follow what you are doing. Also remember that cattle judging is taken very seriously, and while most exhibitors will forgive a judge who gets the placings wrong because he doesn't know any better, they will take a very dim view of him, if puts up his friends, or puts down his enemies.

Methods of judging

The most common and easiest to follow method of judging is to let the animals go round the ring a couple of times, then to check them individually coming towards you and going away from you, to see if there are faults with their legs or in the way they walk, it is also advisable to ask the age of the animal at this stage, especially at smaller shows with few entries, where classes are sometimes amalgamated Always make sure that you give every animal the same amount of attention at this stage, because it is soul-destroying for an exhibitor when an animal that has taken months to prepare for a show, is completely ignored by the judge.

When you have a rough idea of how you are going to place the animals, line them up in order of merit from left to right, making sure that if there is a slope in the ring, that they are standing with their heads uphill.

Once lined up you can then make any adjustments to the line up that are necessary, and, to be absolutely sure that you have got it right, walk them once more round the ring, before lining them up and giving out the prize tickets.

When judging summer shows, judges are required to place all the animals in the class in order of merit. However at pre-sale shows, where there are large numbers of animals to be judged indoors and class sizes are determined by the number of animals that the show ring will accommodate (about fifteen), the usual procedure when judging is to line up a short leet of the seven best animals in the class, then ask the others to leave the ring. This leaves more space for the final placings to be made.

Good points
As the aim of most beef breeders is to produce animals with the highest proportion of their meat where the most expensive cuts are, the animal with the straightest top line, best spring of rib, and biggest back end, should go to the top of the class, provided that it is not too fat, and is good on its feet.

But there is also one other feature that has to be taken into consideration when judging, and that is character. Character is something that cannot be measured, or weighed, and is very difficult to describe. The easiest way for me to describe it, is for you to picture members of the opposite sex passing you in the street. Every now and then, one will pass who, although no more good looking than the others, will attract your attention because of the proud, regal way they walk, that's "character".

First impressions are usually the correct ones, so try not to make too many changes. The more you make, the bigger a muddle you will get into. If you do get in a muddle, never ask the ring steward for advice, as most exhibitors hate to see a judge conferring with the ring steward before making his decisions. It's far better to give out the tickets and get the class out of the ring, and hope that the next class will be easier.

Faults

The most difficult part of judging is in deciding how hard to penalise faults. As far as I am concerned the most serious faults are cattle that are overfed, (especially heifers), and ones that are bad on their hind legs. It is very difficult for anyone who has never fed show cattle themselves, to appreciate the skill that is needed to bring an animal out to its "peak of perfection" for the day of the show, whereas it is very easy to put them "over the top" and it is for this reason, that if it came to a close decision, I would put up the one that was not overfed every time.

Animals that are seriously over fat; show signs of lamenitis; or are lame, should be put to the bottom of the class. Small bumps and blemishes should not be taken too seriously, except when it comes to a close decision, then preference should be given to the one without them.

When it comes to judging the championship I would put a senior cow in milk, in front of a dry cow or heifer of equal merit, because much more skill and effort is needed to bring out a cow in milk, plus the fact that a cow in milk has to feed her calf as well as herself.

Judging Interbreed Championships

Judges of interbreed competitions need to have a fair knowledge of all breeds to enable them to assess which animal is the most outstanding representative of its own breed.

Giving reasons

At some of the major shows, when the judges finish each class, they may be asked to give the ringside spectators their reason for the order of merit in which they placed the animals. When doing this it is always better to comment on the good points of the animals rather than their faults, as some breeders take serious offence at any criticism of their animals.

Stewarding - *Line Stewards*

Most breed societies have a policy of asking their members to take their turn at stewarding shows and sales. This is a task that should be taken seriously, as it is very frustrating for both the judge and the exhibitors if the stewarding is not done properly.

If you are asked to be a line steward, then your duty is to get each class of animals from the cattle lines to the judging ring and have them in catalogue order when they enter the ring. To do this you will need to allow yourself sufficient time before judging starts to meet the exhibitors, and check to see if all the animals they entered are forward for showing.

Any animals not present should be stroked off the catalogue, and their numbers given to the ring steward so that he can stroke them from his catalogue as well. Always keep the exhibitors informed of any changes to the time the judging will start, so that they can adjust their preparations accordingly.

At small shows, exhibitors are usually allowed time to take the animal they have been showing in one class, back to its stall, before bringing out the one in the next class. Most exhibitors do a quick changeover, but there is always the odd one or two who think the whole show is being run for their convenience. They spends extra time on their animals, to the frustration of the other exhibitors, and the spectators waiting for the class to come into the ring . It is up to the line steward to see that not too much time is wasted between classes.

When all the classes have been finished it is then time to judge the male and female champions and, depending on the order in which they were judged, either all the first prize males or first prize females should be brought into the ring.

Whenever the champion of either section is picked, the second prize animal in the same class should be taken into the ring to be judged against the other first prize winners for the reserve championship prize because there is always the possibility that the two best males or the two best females are in the same class.

Once the male and female championships have been decided, they have then to be judged against one another for the supreme championship. Here again, because there is a chance that the two best animals are in the same section, once the supreme championship has been decided, the reserve champion from that section has to come into the ring to compete for the reserve overall championship award.

After the supreme championship judging is completed there are often some special prizes to be judged. Usually there is one for the best animal "bred by exhibitor". It is the highest placed exhibitor-bred animal in each class that is eligible to compete for this prize, even if it was only third or fourth in its class, as is often the case in senior cow classes, where a lot of the animals have been bought specially for showing.

A line steward should be aware of what animals will need to be brought forward for the special prizes, and have them at the ring-side ready for when they are needed for judging. Otherwise a lot of time can be lost trying to find them and get them from the sheds to the ring.

At major shows and sales where large numbers of cattle are forward and there are a lot of classes to be judged, stewards really need to be "on the ball" so that as soon as one class has been judged the next one is ready to enter the ring. Line stewards can save themselves a lot of running about looking for cattle at major shows, if they have a diagram of where each breeder's cattle are standing in the cattle sheds.

Ring Stewards

If you are a ring steward your job is to make sure that each class comes into the ring in the catalogue order, and goes round the ring in a clockwise direction. You also need to check with the line steward to make sure that all the animals in the class are in the ring before asking the judge to start.

While the class is being judged, pay attention to what is going on in the ring, and if any stockman is having trouble getting his animal to go, give it a chase on. Also pay attention to the judge in case he needs the animals to be lined up in a certain way, or wants information regarding their age from the catalogue.

After the prizes have been handed out, and their numbers are entered in the judge's book, it is customary for the class to be paraded once round the ring in the order in which they were placed.

Ring stewards also need to keep a check on all animals eligible for special prizes, and pass their numbers on to the line steward who can then have the required animals forward when it is time for them to be judged, For while most experienced stockmen who think they have a chance of winning a special prize, will be aware of the situation and have their animal ready, there is always the one who, on being awarded a second prize, forgets that his animal will be needed for the reserve championship awards and wanders off to watch the judging, or goes to the bar to drown his sorrows, making it very hard for him to be found when he is needed.

When it comes to stewarding interbreed championships, where the champion and reserve of each breed is eligible to compete, always judge the champions first. Only when the overall supreme championship has been decided, should the reserve champion of the same breed be brought into the ring to compete against the other breed champions for the reserve overall supreme championship award.

If all the champions, and reserves, are taken into the ring together, the judge is then obliged to pick the overall supreme champion from the animals put in front of him, with the chance that he will put one of the reserve champions up, thus not only embarrassing the judge who judged the section, but the breeders involved as well.

Etiquette at shows & sales

This is easiest summed up by saying, *"do as you would be done by"*.

Firstly, if you are going to a show or sale, try and arrive in decent time. It's very annoying for exhibitors with all their animals washed and settled in, when someone arrives late, usually with animals with green muck pouring out of them and upsetting all the others for the next couple of hours, while the owner proudly states, that they were only taken out of the field that morning.

If you arrive early at a show with your animals, don't wash them in someone else's stalls, and make sure that you tie them up properly so they don't annoy the person next to you by turning round and making a mess of his animals or eating their feed. Never feed or water anybody else's animals unless you are asked to by the person in charge of them, and if they are lying down don't make them get up unless you have a good reason. Don't point out faults in other folks cattle to buyers in order to try and sell your own.

Try to have an understanding with the persons in charge of the animals on either side of you whereby you throw out any muck from under each others animals if the others are not there.

Always muck out first thing in the morning to enable the show staff to get it cleared before the show opens for the day. This is especially important at major shows like the Highland and the Royal, where large amounts of muck have to be moved before a specific time.

If you are exercising or washing in the evening, try and get it done in good time, rather than starting about ten o'clock (as some folk do) disturbing all the other animals in the shed.

While in the judging ring, don't crowd the animal in front of you, and when the judge pulls you in, don't barge in to your place, try and do it tidily. If you are placed further down the line than you expected, try not to show your disappointment, (it's so obvious to the spectators) and whatever you do, don't say anything derogatory to the judge. Always bear in mind that you may be judged by the same person sometime in the future, and while what you have said will not affect how he places your animals at the next show, you may however, not get the "benefit of the doubt" if it comes to a close decision.

When making your way back from the judging ring to the cattle sheds try not to let your animal rub up against any animals in the next class that are done up ready to go into the ring. During parades in the grand ring, remember that the whole point of showing is to advertise, not only your own herd, but also your breed. So don't lie down on the grass while the parade is assembling. Not only does it look untidy, but you have every chance of getting trampled on if an animal runs away.

If you are lucky enough to have a champion and have the honour of leading your breed in the parade, always check behind you to see that the others are keeping up. If not, slow down to let them catch up, as a space between breeds doesn't look nearly so bad as space in the middle of one.

Handling & halter training

Handling

Cattle, like children and dogs, need to be handled firmly from an early age. If you can't control them when they are young, it is all the more difficult the older they get.

Cattle are easily frightened by people shouting, or running past them, so always make a habit of speaking to them as you approach, to make them aware of your presence. Try to teach children that are in contact with cattle, how important it is not to run past them or make any sudden movements.

While I am not in favour of giving animals a "hiding", they should however be made aware that a piece of polythene pipe hurts, and should be checked any time they get out of line, especially young bulls that try to face up to you.

Halter training

The most important thing to remember when training or leading animals is *never ever* wrap the rope round your hand: otherwise if the animal runs away and you lose your footing, there is every chance that you will get dragged along behind it. Always let go of the rope if you fall, there are no medals for would-be heroes who hang on to a rope after falling, and get dragged along the ground behind an animal. I know of several cases where people have been seriously hurt in this way.

Try to find time every year to halter-train all young stock, or at least tie them up with a halter and groom them for ten minutes every day for a week. To catch them, they can either be run through the race, or lassoed.

Lasooing cattle is not so difficult as you might think. Most people are able to have a reasonable success rate within half an hour. When you get the loop around the animal's neck put the rope round a post and pull the animal in tight to it before trying to put on the halter. If an animal struggles too much and begins to choke, be ready to slacken off the rope straight away. Always tie halters with a slip knot so that it can be undone quickly in an emergency.

The big advantage of catching cattle with a lasso, is, that once they have been caught a couple of times they learn that they are not going to get away. After that they don't struggle too much when they feel the rope around their neck. This means that individual animals can be caught in the yards, or fields, without the whole group having to be run through the race.

Once all the animals in the group are tied up, groom them. This the best way to gain an animal's confidence. After a couple of sessions you should be able to approach, without them struggling and trying to get away.

All cattle should be taught to move when you pull on the halter, rather than having someone chasing them up from behind all the time. otherwise it can be very hard work when you have to lead them out on your own. If the animals are not too big, usually one person can teach them by putting strain on the rope and holding it until the animal moves forward. Keep repeating the process until the animal gets the hang of it. Try not to let the animals get away from you, because if they get away once or twice it is very difficult to get them out of the habit. For this reason it is best to train animals in an area where, if they do get away, they can't go too far. It also pays to put an extra length of rope on the end of the halter to make it easier to catch any that do get away.

When two or more people are halter training an animal, they should all be pulling on the same rope. In this way they will be able to turn the animals head round and have more chance of holding it. If ropes are put on both sides of the animal this enables it to keep pulling straight making it almost impossible to hold it.

When teaching animals to lead with a ring or bull-dog in their nose, don't pull on their noses for the first couple of times out. Most animals of reasonable temperament can be halter-trained by leading them out for ten minutes each day for a week.

Handling old bulls

Firstly, always treat old bulls with respect and never trust them completely. When bulls get to about two years old I always think they resemble fourteen year old sons and will push you to see just how much they can get away with. Being too old to have a show-down with, the art is to get them to do what you want without either of you losing face.
Each old bull has a character of his own and has to be treated as an individual. While some are co-operative and can be caught in the field or taken away from the cows without any trouble, others are just the opposite.

If the stock bull is not running with the cows and one has to be served it is always best to tie her up; lead the bull to her and let him serve her a couple of times; then lead him back to his pen. This saves the problem of having to try and separate the bull from the cow, to get him back to his pen.

When the bull is running with a cow in season, and you want to separate them, it's always best to run the cow back with him to his pen. It's always easier to slip the cow out from the bull, rather than the other way round. The same applies when you want to take a bull away from cows in season in the field, always take in the whole group rather than trying to take the bull in on his own.

Some old bulls are very possessive when they are running with the cows and will not tolerate any bull calves near a cow that is in season. It is not uncommon for bull calves to be severely injured or even killed because of this. When two old bulls start fighting don't try to stop them. If you do manage to stop them (without getting yourself hurt) they will only keep niggling at each other until they can have another go and sort out who is boss.

Bulls that are hard to catch should have a piece of light chain about a foot long, attached to their ring. This can then be caught with a piece of fencing wire with a hook in it. Any bull that has made a serious attempt to attacked someone, should never be trusted again, as sooner or later it will have another go. Such bulls are best got rid of, for to misquote the safety rhyme from shooting, "all the best bulls ever bred, won't repay for one man dead"

Exercising

The amount of exercising needed, depends on how the animals are housed. If they are in small individual pens and being fed hard for shows or sales, they will need to be either led out on a halter, or turned out in a paddock every day. Bulls that are housed in groups need less exercising as the move around the pen a lot more.

When groups of bulls are being fed all summer for selling at the autumn sales, it is often best to run them out in a paddock all night. This will not only keep them right on their legs, but as the nights get colder, towards Autumn, they will grow good coats of hair. A good coat of hair can hide a multitude of faults.

Where large numbers of bulls are being run together in groups and there are not enough paddocks to accommodate them all, erect an electric fence around a paddock about five yards in from the perimeter fence. Bulls can then be driven round the alley way between the two fences one group at a time. The only snag with this system is that if there has been a lot of rain it gets a bit muddy under foot, and while this does the bulls no harm, it makes it hard work for the person chasing them round. If bulls running together in groups, are exercised regularly every day, this will go a long way to reducing the incidence of riding and fighting.

Mechanical exercising machines driven by electric motors are available, but at present most are used at AI stations for exercising old bulls.

Foot trimming

The importance of keeping the feet of pedigree animals well-trimmed cannot be over emphasised, so make a habit of trimming all the cows' feet before they are turned out to grass in the spring. Having been standing on muck all winter their feet will have grown a lot and be out of shape. The muck also softens the feet and makes them a lot easier to trim at this time of year, whereas if they are left until the cows have been out at the grass for a month or two their feet become very hard and it also becomes a very messy job with all the green muck flying around.

All animals going to shows or sales should have their feet trimmed about six weeks before the event. To avoid leaving rope marks, wrap a piece of sacking round their legs before putting on the ropes. It also pays to stand the animals in a foot bath, filled with a solution of formalin for a few minutes each day, the week prior to going to the show. This hardens the feet and reduces the chances of them going lame.

Unless you have been trained to trim feet, and have a crush made specially for foot trimming, it is best to call in a contractor to do the job There are quite a few contractors doing foot trimming and prices are very competitive, particularly when large numbers have to be done.

There are two different ways of restraining cattle while foot trimming. The traditional way is to put them in a crush specially made for the job, where the animal is done standing, with webs under its belly to support it, The foot is lifted and tied to a wooden plank and pared with a wood chisel. The other is where the animal is put in a crush, webs put under it, then the crush is turned over on its side by means of a hydraulic ram. The feet are then trimmed with an electric grinder while the animal is lying on its side.

Because the skill of foot trimming cannot be learned from a book, I will make no attempt to describe how it should be done, other than to suggest that you either go on a course, or watch a skilled operator, before trying to do it yourself.

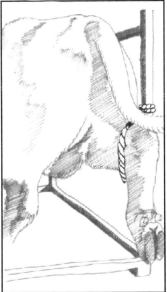

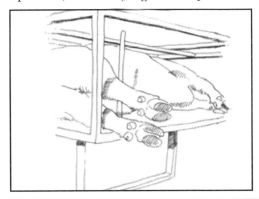

Chapter three

Pedigrees & genes

Pedigree animals are ones whose parentage has been recorded over a number of generations, with details of their date of birth; their sires and dams,etc, being registered in a herd book.

What has to be realised is that a pedigree is only a record of the animal's parentage, and that it is the quality of animals named in the pedigree as far back as their great-grandparents, that is relevant, not the length of it.

This diagram is an example of line breeding, Ewan being the common Grandparent to both Champion's Sire and Dam.

		G.G.S. **Jock**
	Grand sire **Hamish**	
		G.G.D. **Jill**
Sire **Hector**		
		G.G.S. **Ewan**
	Grand Dam **Clara**	
		G.G.D. **Fiona**

Champion

		G.G.S. **Barry**
	Grand Sire **Dougal**	
		G.G.D. **Eloiese**
Dam **Catriona**		
		G.G.S. **Ewan**
	Grand Dam **Melody**	
		G.G.D. **Helen**

Abbreviations: G.G.S Great Grand Sire. G.G.D. Great Grand Dam.

A common mistake when studying pedigrees is to concentrate on the one or two very good animals named in the pedigree, and ignore the four or five bad ones, especially if there are bad ones on both the sire's and dam's side of the pedigree.

In order to establish a herd of females of a desired type, some breeders line breed to the outstanding sires or dams in their herd. To do this they mate two animals that have a common outstanding grandparent. This has the advantage in that there is more chance of the best characteristics being inherited.

Line breeding should only be practised with animals that are structurally sound. Otherwise there is every chance that any faults they have will be exaggerated in their offspring and be very hard to breed out. *(See example on page 55.)*

Genes

Genes are the hereditary factors in an animal that decide its size, shape, colour etc. It is by matching animals of similar stature that it is possible to produce animals of uniform conformation.

On the other hand by pairing animals of contrasting conformation, the stature of the resulting offspring are less predictable as it is dependent on which parent has the more dominant genes.

An example of this can be found, if, for instance, a very dominant polled breed such as British White, is mated with a dominant beef breed of horned cattle such as the British Charolais. The first generation of calves will inherit an increased size and fleshing ability from the genes of their father, but will still be polled because of the dominant poll genes of their mother.

Subsequent mating of the offspring with horned beef sires will reduce the influence of the poll gene, until after about four generations the horned gene will be dominant.

Keeping records

Keeping accurate records is absolutely essential when breeding pedigree cattle. With the use of artificial insemination (AI) and a gestation period of over nine months, it is all to easy to forget who was served with what and when; with the result that when the off-spring are blood typed for proof of parentage (a requirement of some breed societies), they don't always match.

Current government regulations require that a record is kept of any movement of cattle on and off the farm; the parentage of all calves born; and any drugs that are administered to cattle. These records need to be kept up to date as officials from the Ministry of Agriculture Fisheries and Food (MAFF) have the power to inspect them at any time. Breed societies' rules also require that records are kept of dates of birth, service and artificial inseminations dates etc.

It is always best to keep records in the simplest way possible, This allows more chance of them being kept up to date. The simplest way that I have found, is to use A4 hardback exercise books, which can be kept out in the buildings, and filled in whenever an animal has been inseminated, served, calved or injected. This information can then, if necessary, be transferred to a computer on a weekly basis. or duplicated and filed in the office as a back up system.

Service dates
Service dates should be filled in (one to a line) underneath one another. Then if a cow comes back in season three weeks after her last service, just put a line through the previous service date and write in the new one at the bottom of the list.

The advantage of doing them this way, is that if a cow calves a full-time calf, six weeks earlier than expected (as often happens as the result of an animal being re-inseminated or served when they are in an early state of pregnancy), it is easy to check back and see who the sire was.

Or if a cow comes in season again three weeks after she was served, it is very easy to check back and see which bull she was mated with, and what medication she was given the last time she was in season.

Example of service dates records

Date:	Dam:	Sire:	Type:	Notes:	Due:
17 March	Mary	Viceroy	A.I.	xx	xx
20 March	June	Valliant	A.I.		4 January
2 April	Jane	Valliant	N.S.	w.o.i.	16 January
6 April	Diana	Valliant	N.S.	m.v.	20 January
8 April	Daisy	Sultan	A.I.		xx
8 Apri	Mary	Valliant	N.S.	w.o.i.	22 January
l8 April	Maud	Sultan	A.I.		23 January
23 April	Jennifer	Valliant	N.S.	+p.m.	7 February
28 April	Daisy	Valliant	N.S.	+a.m.,w.o.i	xx

Abbreviations

A.I.	Artificial insemination	**w.o.i.**	Washed out with iodine
+a.m.	Inseminated again the next morning	**m.vi.**	Multi-vitamin injection
+p.m.	Inseminated again in the afternoon	**xx**	Repeat service

Put in "due" dates after they go 6 weeks with no repeat service. This makes it easier when making out the calving list.

Calving records

Calving records can be kept in the same way as service dates. It is always best to put in details of all calvings whether alive, dead, or premature, as this makes it easier to fill in any census forms sent out by MAFF which require the total numbers of calvings.

Example of calving records

D.O.B.:	Dam:	Sire:	b.w.:	Sex:	Name:	No:	Comments:
14 January	June	Victor	45 kg	M	Nelson	N1	
16 January	Jane	Vince	42 kg	F	xx	x	dead
20 January	Mary	Victor	50 kg	M	Nero	n2	
22 January	Maud	Sultan	45 kg	F	Naomi	N3	
23 January	Jenny	Sultan	65 kg	M	Nugget	N4	Caesar
7 February	Diana	Victor	42 kg	F	Natalie	N5	

Record of goods on and off the farm

"On-and-off" sheets are useful in situations where the stockman can buy goods from suppliers on account, and where the accounts and main book keeping is done by another person.

A4 size books with carbon copies are available for this purpose. If records are totalled weekly by the stockman, and he gives the top sheet to the bookkeeper while retaining the copy. This minimises the chance of mistakes being made.

Example of an On and Off sheet

Fantasy Farm Week ending 10 February 1996

Goods on

Date	Supplier	Goods
3.2.96	E. JonesGoods	value £56
6.2.96	Bibby	Sup.2100 kg dairy meal
8.2.96	J.Bloggs	10-25 kg bags minerals
9.2.96	M.F. Perth	1 Bull EAR NO. GOOD-1

Goods off

Date	Delivered to	Goods
3.2.96	E.Smith	1 Tractor Reg.USE-LESS Scrap
7.2.96	M.F. Perth	3 Bulls Ear. No.J-1, J-3, J-6
8.2.96	Kennels	1 cow Ear.No. DEAD-1

Example of DIY Semen record

DIY Semen delivery and use records

Sire	Delivery date	Purchased from	Number of straws
Sultan	1.2.96.	A Smith	1 2 3 4 5 6 7 8 9 10 11 12
Valliant	4.5.96.	R Jones	1 2 3 4 5 6 7 8 9 10
Viceroy	5.9.96.	G Evans	1 2 3 4 5 6 7 8 9 10 11 12

Each time a straw is used it should be crossed off the end of the list. This will make it possible to see at a glance how many are left.

Animal movement records (mandatory)

Regulations (at the time of writing) require that a record must be kept of all animal movements. Your local MAFF office will provide books for this purpose, and they have to be kept up to date. MAFF officials are entitled to inspect them any time. The reason for keeping a record of animal movements is, that if an outbreak of any infectious disease occurs, it is possible to trace any animals that have been in contact with the disease.

Records of medicines (mandatory)

Regulations (at the time of writing) also require that a record must be kept of all drugs given to cattle. Your local MAFF office will send you a book for this purpose. Vets are not allowed to supply drugs such as penicillin, or tetramycin, for stockmen to administer themselves, without having first examined the animals and diagnosed the ailment. They must also be sure that the stockman will keep a record of all drugs used and is aware that if the drugs are not administered as prescribed, there is a possibility of the bacteria becoming drug resistant.

Keep old records

Never throw away old diaries or records. Even if they are never needed again, at least they will make interesting reading in years to come.

Transporting cattle

Regulations (at the time of writing) require that all lorries and trailers have to be fitted with partitions a maximum of 3.1 metres apart and that a certificate of transportation with details of the animals and the time and date of loading; etc. has to accompany the animals throughout their journey

Vehicles pulling small trailers outside a certain radius from their base are required to be fitted with a tachograph. There is also a limit on the weight that can be towed, relative to the weight of the vehicle towing it.

Beware of overloading. Roadside checks by police are very common, both day and night. It is worth remembering that if you are pulling a caravan behind your lorry, the weight of the caravan comes into the calculations for the total "train weight" of the vehicle. (check with the Ministry of Transport).

It is also worth remembering, that if you have been drinking heavily at a show, you may not pass a breathalyser test for more than 24 hours after your last drink.

Cattle always seem to travel best in large articulated lorries, as there is less sway in them than in rigids or small trailers. Cattle also travel well on double deckers, but extra care must be taken when unloading the top deck because of the steep ramp. It is often best to untie the animals and let them come down the ramp on their own.

Some cattle get very upset when transported in small trailers without company, probably because it's often the very first time in its life that the animal has been completely alone. To overcome this it is often best to pen up the animal on its own for a week or so before transportation.

Care must be taken to ensure that the tow bar on the towing vehicle is at the correct height for the trailer. Otherwise, not only will it make the combination unsafe when braking, but it will increase the chances of having "blowouts" in the tyres.

It is very important to distribute the weight correctly in the trailer. Too much weight on the draw bar will take the weight off the front of the towing vehicle making it difficult to control if you have to brake hard, while too much weight on the back of the trailer will cause it to sway, even at very low speeds.

If an animal you buy at a sale and take home on its own in a small trailer gets upset and shows signs of being difficult to unload, the safest way to deal with it is to back the trailer up to a pen within sight of other cattle, then cut the halter from the outside and let the animal run into the pen on its own. In most cases the animal will settle down within ten minutes.

Cattle that are to be transported to shows or sales should have their diet restricted to hay and water for 24 hours before travelling, otherwise if they have a stomach full of high protein feeding, and don't chew their cud,the feeding will start to ferment in their stomach and make them sick.

Lorries and trailers with alloy bodies can leave stains if animals rub on them when travelling over long distances, so it pays to put a strip of hessian sacking along behind the animals as this will save an awful lot of washing when you get to your destination.

When loading cattle always put plenty of straw on the ramp, and load the quietest one first, as there will be less chance of it panicking if it's left on its own in the lorry when you are unloading. Animals that are a bit nervous are best put in the middle of the load so that when they come off the lorry they will see their mates and settle down quicker.

Animals should be tied fairly short in the lorry so that there is less chance of them putting a foot over the rope or trying to fight the others, also make sure that the halters fit properly and won't slip off during the journey.

Always drive steadily for the first ten miles or so to give the animals a chance to get used to the sway of the lorry, and leave enough room between you and the vehicle in front so that you don't have to do emergency stops.

When starting up after coffee or lunch breaks make sure that all the animals are on their feet before you move off, otherwise there is a chance that the ones that are lying may get trampled on.

When unloading always back right up to the gate of the pen or shed, so that any animal that is upset and tries to run away can't run off into open space, remember that the nice quiet animal that you put onto the lorry, may not act the same when you go to take it off.

On arrival at the show or sale, animals should be tied up by the halter on one side, and neck rope on the other, and be fed and watered sparingly for the first 24 hours until their stomachs start working properly again.

If, as sometimes happens, an animal that is completely out of control, has to be loaded onto a lorry, the safest way to go about it, is to attach a long rope to its halter and put it up through the lorry and out through an opening at the front. In this way the rope can be pulled in to prevent the animal from turning back and attacking the person chasing it up from behind.

Fertilised ovum transplants (FOT)

Because of modern technology it is now possible to transplant fertilised eggs from pure-bred cows into surrogate cross-bred mothers to produce pure-bred calves, whose parentage can be confirmed by blood typing.

It is also possible to freeze and store the fertilised eggs by the same procedure as that used for semen, Conception rates from frozen eggs are comparable to that of fresh ones. Both the recovery of the eggs from the donor cow, and transplantation of them into the recipient, can be done non-surgically on the farm, or, if preferred, at an embryo centre.

The procedure is to inject the donor cow with super ovulation drugs at a certain stage in her breeding cycle which will induce her produce a number of eggs. When she comes in season she is either served naturally or inseminated. Seven days later the eggs will have made their way down from the ovaries to the horns of the womb. It is at this stage that they are recovered, by flushing out the horns of the womb with a fluid solution.

By this method, it is sometimes possible to get more than twenty eggs from one flushing, but because cows vary greatly in their response to super-ovulation drugs, results can vary considerably. The average number of top grade eggs, per cow flushed, is about six.

This procedure should not be seen as a means of rapid multiplication, but as a way of getting a few extra calves out of some of the most important cows in the herd, whose progeny will not only be of benefit to the breeder, but to the breed as a whole.

Most breed societies have special rules concerning FOT calves, and usually charge higher fees for registering them, in order to discourage breeders from flushing anything other than their best cows.

Flushing freshly calved cows

When flushing freshly calved cows, it is always best to give them a chance to build up their condition for two or three months after calving before any attempt is made to flush them. If the flushing is a success they can be put back in calf, and if necessary the same procedure repeated after their next calving.

Flushing stale dry cows

It is often possible to recover fertilised eggs from cows that cannot be got in calf. This can be a way of getting an extra calf or two out of a valuable cow. Best flushing results are obtained when animals are on a rising plane of condition, so if a stale cow is flushed once or twice without success, it is often worth while slimming her down before trying her again when she is being built back up into condition, Alternatively leave her out all winter and try her again in the spring.

Recipients

Regulations mandate that fertilised eggs are only put into recipients capable of calving the resulting calves. Therefore eggs from the larger continental breeds should only be transplanted into big strong recipients, preferably ones that have calved at least once naturally.

When the transplantation is being done at an embryo centre, they usually supply the recipients. This can be advantageous in that you only have to buy the ones that are in calf. The disadvantage is that you do not know where they came from originally. Because of this many breeders prefer to buy their recipients as a batch from a known source.

If recipient heifers have to be bought in, it is always best to buy them well in advance of when they are needed. This allows them time to get settled in and absorb any vitamins or trace elements they are given to help conception,

Where only one donor cow is to be flushed and you have no eggs in storage, it is often best to flush the donor to see if she is going to produce eggs, before buying recipients. If the flushing is successful the eggs can be frozen and stored. You can then buy recipients with the knowledge that if they are synchronised to match the donor for the next flushing and the flushing is not a success, the frozen eggs can be put in instead.

One advantage of having recipients synchronised to match the donor is that if eggs recovered from the flushing are not suitable for freezing, they can be put straight into the recipients.

Recipients that are calving for the first time, will need to be checked regularly when they come to calving, as there is always the possibility that some of the calves will be too big for them to calve, necessitating a caesarian operation.

Skeletal faults in cattle

Skeletal abnormalities in newborn calves
A) *Front legs bent forward at the knee*

This becomes more apparent after the calf is about three days old and if left untreated gets gradually worse. It is caused by a lack of vitamin E and usually responds well to a course of vitamin E and selenium. It has been my experience that treating affected calves with multi-vitamins aggravates the situation. Injecting cows six weeks before they calve with selenium reduces the problem considerably. (consult your vet.)

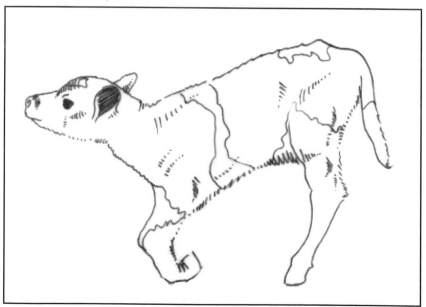

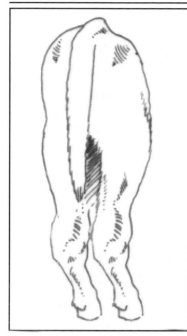

B) Back legs bent sideways at the hocks but in the same direction

This is common in very large calves, especially ones that are born back-to-front. It seems to be caused by the position in which the calf is lying in the womb. This is nothing to worry about as affected animals may sometimes look a disaster but usually come right without treatment within a couple of weeks.

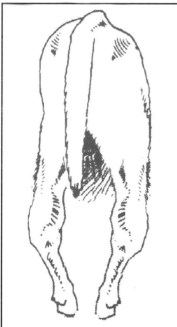

C) Back legs bent sideways at the hocks but in opposite directions

Whilst you often get calves that walk wide when they are newborn, this condition is different and quite noticeable, with the calf often being unable to stand on its own. This problem does not respond to treatment and should be seen as a genetic fault, especially if there are a number of calves showing the same symptoms that are all by the same sire.

Serious consideration should given as to whether to continue using the sire.

D) Calves born with short tails

Calves that are born with short tails should not be used for pedigree sires because of the possibility of it being a genetic fault, whereby it may not appear in the first generation of the progeny but could reappear in subsequent generations.

E) Twisted mouths in newborn calves

It's quite common for calves to be born with what looks like a deformed mouth, especially if they have had a difficult birth, but this nothing to worry about as they usually come all right after a week or two.

Skeletal faults it adult cattle - Jaws

A) Normal Jaw

The two diagrams below show a normal mouth with the teeth

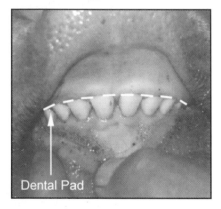
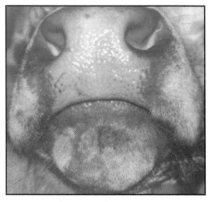

reaching the outer edge of the dental pad.

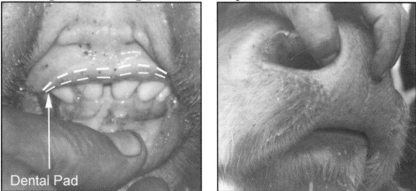

B) Undershot Jaw (Hereditary)

Note how the teeth fail to reach the dental pad. This is a hereditary fault. Any animal showing this defect should not be used for pedigree breeding.

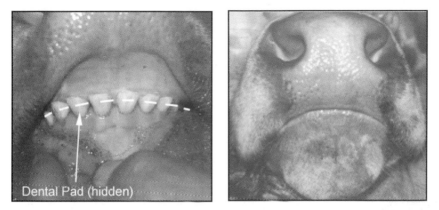

Dental Pad (hidden)

C) Overshot Jaw (Hereditary)

This diagram shows the teeth extending beyond the outer edge of the dental pad.

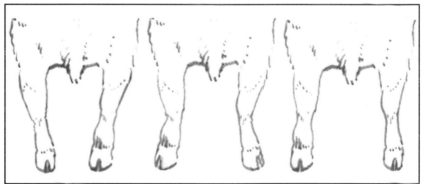

Skeletal faults in front legs (front view)
Di   *Dii*   *Diii*

(Di) **Feet turned in.**

(Dii) **Feet turned out**.

(Diii) **Correct.**

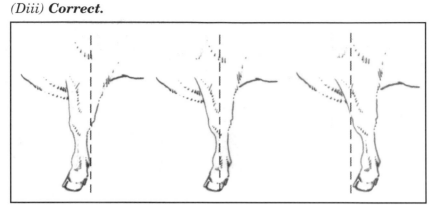

E) Skeletal faults in front legs (side view)
(Ei) **Overstretched**   *(Eii)* **Correct**   *(Eiii)* **Too far back**

Overstretching is often an indication that the animal is suffering from lamenitis through overfeeding.

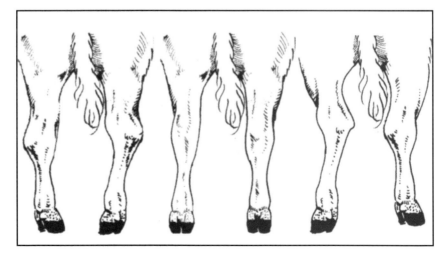

H) Skeletal faults in hind legs (back view)
(Hi) **Hocks too wide** *(Hii)* **Correct**   *(Hiii)* **Hocks too close**

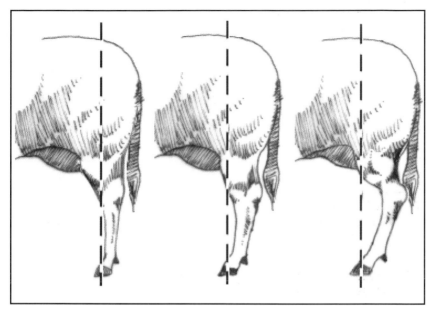

G) Skeletal faults back legs (side view)
(Gi) **Too straight** *(Gii)* **Correct** *(Giii)* **Sycle hock**

H) Skeletal faults in the feet of adult cattle
Deformed feet
Beware of cattle that have small cleats on the outside of either their front or hind feet, as this causes them to walk badly as soon as they start to put on weight. It is hereditary and is more common in some families within breeds than others. Care should be taken that one stock bull with this fault is not followed by another.

I) Shallow heels
This is not a serious problem but one to be aware of. It's more common in continental, than native breeds.

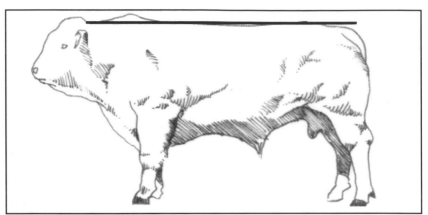

Conformation

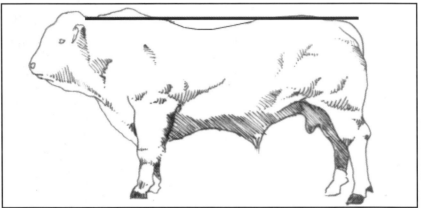

Good conformation
Poor conformation

Diseases & ailments.

Because no drugs should be administered to cattle unless the animal has first been examined by a veterinary surgeon to establish the nature of the ailment, this chapter is written with the intention of helping beginners recognise and prevent diseases and ailments, rather than cure them.

Diseases

Ministry of Agriculture Fisheries and Food (MAFF) regulations require that all herds of cattle in the United Kingdom have to be tested periodically for tuberculosis and brucellosis.

Voluntary, "Elite Health" schemes are available where, in addition to tuberculosis and brucellosis the herd is periodically tested for Enzootic Bovine lucosis (EBL); Infectious Bovine Rinotracheitis (IBR) and Leptospirosis. Elite herd status is an advantage when exporting cattle. Major shows and sales specify that all entries are from EBL free herds.

Notifiable diseases are those, where any animal suspected of having the disease must be notified to the Ministry of Agriculture Fisheries and Food (MAFF).

Anthrax (notifiable) (Rare in the UK)
Symptoms
Animals suffering from this disease usually show no symptoms and most often are found lying dead. Animals that have died from the disease will often show signs of haemorrhaging from their external orifices.

Because anthrax can be transmitted to other species, including humans, through contact with the dead animal's blood, any animal found dead for no obvious reason must be notified to MAFF they will arrange for a sample of blood to be taken and tested for anthrax before the carcass can be moved. Because anthrax spores can lie dormant in the soil for a great number of years, infected carcasses have to be either incinerated or buried in lime.

Cause
Most cases in this country are traced back to imported feeding, usually cotton cake.

Cure
Because of the nature of the disease there is no cure. Severe restrictions will be imposed on both animals and humans entering or leaving the premises where the disease is suspected.

Brucellosis (notifiable) (Compulsory annual test)
Symptoms

It is rare for animals to abort from brucellosis in the UK. Animals will abort their calves about 8 to 12 weeks before they are due and usually retain the cleansing, which will be very messy and smelly. Being contagious, a number of animals will abort within a matter of weeks.

Treatment
Any animals reacting positive to brucellosis are required to be slaughtered, and movement restrictions will be imposed on the remainder of the herd until it has passed two clear tests.

Prevention
All abortions should be taken seriously, and must be notified to MAFF. Any animal that looks like if it is going to abort, should be put in isolation straight away. Always dip your feet in a foot bath of disinfectant any time you have been in contact with the animal to reduce the chances of spreading the infection.

Bovine Spongiform Encephalopathy (BSE) (notifiable)
Symptoms
This is a progressive disease, with the animal gradually getting more nervous and unsteady on its feet over a period of weeks or months, until eventually it is unable to stand.

Cause
The disease is not yet (at the time of writing) fully understood, but is believed to be caused by contaminated feeding.

Cure
(At the time of writing) no cure is available. Any animal suspected of having the disease should be notified to the MAFF who will arrange for it to be slaughtered.

Bovine Viral Diarrhoea (BVD)
Symptoms
Scouring, particularly in older cows. Adult cattle can be affected in various ways; some will abort while others may have serious fertility problems.

Treatment
Being a virus there is no cure. Antibiotics may be helpful in scouring episodes. Because of potential effects on fertility, any persistent

scouring should be investigated by a vet.

Prevention

In herds where there is a large incidence of the disease it may be beneficial to vaccinate the entire herd.

Foot and mouth (virus) (Notifiable) (Rare in UK)

Symptoms

Infected animals will have blisters on their mouths and tongues. They will also become lame and have blisters on their feet.

Treatment

United Kingdom government policy states that all animals including sheep and pigs on the infected farm are slaughtered on the premises. Restrictions will put on all movements of people and vehicles on and off the premises

Because the virus is airborne and highly infectious, restrictions are also put on the movement of all cattle, sheep and pigs within a three mile radius of the outbreak. All vehicles carrying cattle sheep or pigs en-route will also be restricted from travelling through the restricted area.

Prevention

Vaccinations are available but are banned in the UK. Whenever there is a report of a suspected outbreak, restrict your contact with other farms and disinfect the wheels of vehicles entering the farm, especially delivery lorries.

Infectious Bovine Rinotracheitis (IBR) (virus)

Symptoms

IBR has the same symptoms as pneumonia but is more virulent with higher mortality rates. It is seen more often in adult cattle.

Treatment

Being a virus there is no specific treatment. Antibiotics are useful to prevent secondary bacterial pneumonia developing. Major outbreaks in adult cattle can be devastating.

Prevention

Vaccinations by nasal sprays go a long way towards reducing the incidence of the disease.

Tuberculosis (TB) (compulsory periodic test)

Symptoms

As cattle are tested for tuberculosis on a regular basis, the disease is usually diagnosed by testing before any clinical signs are apparent.

This disease was thought to be almost eradicated throughout the world both in cattle and humans, but is now reappearing in a more virulent strain. Badgers and deer are suspected of being carriers of the disease.

Cure

Bovine tuberculosis can sometimes be cured by a course of antibiotics but full recovery takes a long time. MAFF policy is that all cattle that react positively to a tuberculin test have to be slaughtered

Movement restrictions will be placed on the remainder of the herd until it has passed two clear tests

Virus Pneumonia

Symptoms

Virus pneumonia is usually confined to animals under 18 months of age that are housed inside over the winter. They will stop eating, have a high temperature and a nasal discharge and their breathing will become very rapid. Being very contagious, usually most of the animals in the group will become affected.

Treatment

True virus pneumonia does not respond to antibiotics. However, drug treatments given at onset of the infection, before the lungs are too badly damaged, can help limit the effects of an outbreak and prevent secondary bacterial infections from causing further problems.

Prevention

Vaccinations are available against specific viruses, but it is important to give the correct one at the correct time. Housing and ventilation are more important.

The incidence of pneumonia can be greatly reduced if the animals are housed in open fronted yards where there is a good ventilation, and they are not overstocked. If all buildings are mucked out, pressure washed, and disinfected as soon as the cattle are turned out to grass each year, this will help cut down the carry-over of disease from one year to the next.

Joint ill
Symptoms
Joint ill affects calves in the first two weeks of their life, and is usually a follow-on from an infection of the navel. The affected animal will go lame on more than one leg, and on inspection the joints will be found to be very stiff and painful, and will eventually swell up making it very difficult for the calf to move about.

Treatment
A course of antibiotics will help, but once affected calves get to the stage where their joints are badly swollen they seldom make a complete recovery, and in most cases will either die or have to be put down.

Prevention
Make sure that all calves navels are sprayed with iodine or antiseptic solution at birth. Any calf that shows signs of infection in its navel should be given a full course of antibiotics.

Summer mastitis
Symptoms
Summer mastitis is spread by flies, and is most prevalent in late summer in areas where there is a lot of stagnant water. One or more quarters of a dry cow's udder will become very inflamed and painful causing the animal to go off its feed and look very sick.

Treatment
Unless the animal is treated straight away, animals will nearly always lose the infected quarter, and in severe cases may have an abortion or even die. Affected teats need to be milked out and a tube of antibiotics put in them twice a day. In severe cases animals will need a course of antibiotic injections as well.

Prevention
When drying off cows, put a tube of long acting antibiotics in each teat. It is also advisable to use some sort of deterrent spray to keep

the flies off the teats.

Pink eye

Symptoms

Also called Hereford eye, this is another disease spread by flies, and is most common in low lying areas in late summer. The animal's eye will first start watering, then become inflamed, and if left untreated a white spot will form in the centre of the eye.

Treatment

The eye should be treated as soon as possible otherwise there is a chance that the animal will go blind. Antibiotics will need to be put in the eye daily. Alternatively your veterinary surgeon can inject a single dose of antibiotics into the top eyelid.

Black-leg (bacterium)

Black-leg is most common where animals have access to grazing on river banks. It is caused by a bacterium that lives in the soil and is transmitted to animals through any cuts or bruises they receive. Affected animals die very suddenly, and if skinned it will be found that the infection will have spread over a large part of the animal's carcass.

Prevention

A highly successful vaccine is available, and all cattle should be vaccinated routinely in areas where black-leg is prevalent.

Hypomagnecemia (life threatening)

Cause

Hypomagnescemia (staggers) occurs when the magnesium levels in the blood gets too low.

Symptoms

Most cases occur either shortly after the animals are turned out to grass in the spring, or just before they come in again at the back end of the year. The animal (usually a cow in milk) will become very nervous, shake its head, and become unsteady on its feet, eventually falling down unable to get up. This will often will take place within minutes, and in many cases the animal die within hours, if not treated.

Treatment

A 400 ml bottle of mixture of calcium and magnesium is injected into the vein, followed by bottle of magnesium under the skin just behind the shoulder. It is not advisable to put magnesium directly into the vein on its own, as the sudden reaction will often kill the animal. Recovery can sometimes be very dramatic, with an animal that was close to death one minute, getting up and running away the next.

On farms where there is a high incidence of hypomagnescemia, it is advisable to get your vet to teach you how to treat an animal in an emergency. Always keep a couple of bottles of magnesium calcium mixture as a stand by for emergencies.

Prevention
Animals should be given a high magnesium mineral, either incorporated in the feed, or free access, for about a month before being turned out to grass and again at the back end of the year.

Milk fever (life threatening)
Cause
This is not so common in beef cattle as it is in dairy cattle. It is caused by low levels of calcium in the blood.

Symptoms
The symptoms are very similar to those of hypomagnesia except that they usually occur immediately before, or just after calving, and that they are less excitable. One distinguishing feature of milk fever is that the animal usually lies with an S shaped twist in its neck.

Treatment
A 400 ml bottle of calcium is injected into the vein. Recovery can sometimes be spectacular with the animal getting up on its feet within minutes.

Prevention
In herds where milk fever is a problem, injections of vitamin D3 three weeks before cows are due to calve, then again two days before calving will lessen the chances of animals being affected.

Bloat (life threatening)
Bloat in cattle that are being fed concentrates
Symptoms

Bloat can sometimes become an absolute nightmare. It is most common in bulls that are being given a lot of feeding and usually occurs shortly after they are fed, when they will rapidly fill up with gas on the left side.

Treatment

If the animal is only slightly blown, it will sometimes go down again if it is given some hay. If this does not work, dose it with a Bloat drench, or a pint of cooking oil to neutralise the gas in the stomach. (extra care needs to be taken when dosing animals with bloat as it is very easy to choke them). With a bit of luck the bloat will start going down within 15 minutes. If not call the vet.

In cases where the animal is blown up badly and is in distress, it will be necessary to put a stomach tube or a piece of hose pipe right down its throat into its stomach to let the gas out.

If all else fails, the last resort is to use a trocar and cannula to pierce the animal's side and let the gas out that way.

If you are unfortunate enough to have an animal with bloat, be sure to get your vet to teach you the different ways of letting it down, in case it blows up again and you don't have time to wait for him to arrive.

Cure

Because nobody seems to know what causes bloat, there is no positive cure for it, at least if there is, I've never heard of it. Animals that start blowing up, will usually continue to do so on a regular basis unless they are restricted to a diet of hay and water, or turned out to grass. A change in the ingredients that are being fed often helps, as does the inclusion of additives like avopromycin or rumencin.

Bloat in cattle that are on clover pastures

Bloat can sometimes be a big problem on lush clover pastures, especially if hungry cattle are turned out on to it when there is a heavy dew. Problems can also occur on clover pastures on windy days.

Treatment

Affected animals should be treated as described above.

Gut worms (Parasites)

Symptoms

Gut worms usually only affect cattle under two years old that are out at grass, causing them to scour badly and loose condition.

Treatment

Gutworms and Lungworms can be treated with a combined wormer. All cattle under two years old should be treated regularly, according to the manufacturer's recommendations, either by dosing, injection or pour-on. All are equally effective, but the latter is the simplest method to administer as it is simply poured on along the animals back and absorbed through the skin.

Lungworms

Symptoms

Lungworms mostly affect yearling cattle out at grass, causing them to cough badly, especially if they have been running and exerting themselves. If severely affected they may die.

Treatment

Combined wormer.

Prevention

Vaccinations are available for lungworm.

Skin problems

Warts (Virus)

These mostly affect young cattle, and usually appear in places where the animal has cut itself on barbed wire. They are very difficult to get rid of, and unless the animal is going to be sold or shown they are best left alone to run their course when they will wither and drop off.

Treatment

A serum can be made to vaccinate affected animals, but it is not always successful.

Lice (parasites)

Symptoms

First signs of infection are when the animal starts rubbing itself on

rails or the corners of walls.
Treatment
If any animals in a group show signs of lice, treat the whole group
with lice powder or spray them with sheep dip.

Mange (Parasite)
Symptoms
Mange mostly occurs among young stock that are carrying a lot of
hair, and have been sweating badly. The hair will become matted
and form a scab, which if removed, will expose raw skin. However
other conditions can resemble this and veterinary advice should be
sought.

Treatment
Spray with an approved mange dressing, repeat as necessary.

Prevention
To prevent mange in show cattle they should be washed at least
once a week and sprayed with mange dressing once a month. Some
of the combined wormers used for gut and lung worms are also
effective against lice and mange.

Ringworm (fungus)
Symptoms
Ringworm mostly affects young cattle. They will have round bald
spots mainly on their head and neck. It is very contagious, and is
spread by contact between animals, or by them rubbing on wooden
buildings, or old trees, where the spores can lie dormant for years.

Treatment
Ringworm can be treated by spraying the affected parts daily with
an aerosol spray. A more expensive, but effective cure, is to put an
anti-ringworm drug in the feed. This has the added advantage that
all the cattle are treated at the same time, with less chance of re-
infection. It is also possible to vaccinate against ringworm.

Warning
Ringworm is often picked up by humans, so if any children that are
in contact with infected cattle or buildings, develop a rash, and are
taken to a doctor, make the doctor aware of the possibility of it
being ringworm, as many doctors may not have come across ring-

worm and not be aware that it is a fungus.

Lameness

Animals that go lame suddenly but show no signs of swelling around the top of the hoof, usually have a stone or other foreign body between the cleats. Or it may be that the foot has been punctured by a nail or flint.

Treatment

If no foreign body is found between the cleats check the sole of the foot with a foot knife for nails or flints.

Foul of the foot (Bacterium)
Symptoms

This is usually occurs after a lot of rain when the gateways are very muddy. The affected animal will suddenly go very lame and have a lot of swelling immediately around and above the hoof.

Treatment

Foul of the foot responds well to antibiotics, and if the animal is treated straight away it will usually be sound again within 36 hours. Whereas if treatment is delayed allowing the infection to spread to the joints, recovery can be very slow.

Prevention

It is difficult to prevent foul of the foot in the main herd, but individual show animals will benefit from being stood in a foot bath containing a solution of formalin for a few minutes each day, to harden up their feet before going to a show.

Sand cracks
Symptoms

This problem arises in very dry weather, when the cows' feet become very hard. The animal will gradually go very lame, usually in a front foot. On close examination a thin crack will be found in the hoof and although it may not look much, it causes the animal a lot of pain, especially if it extends to the hairline at the top of the foot.

Treatment

Consult your vet or foot trimming contractor.

Prevention

Regular foot trimming reduces, but does not eliminate the problem.

Lamenitis

This is caused by overfeeding. Over a period of time the affected animals will get more and more tender on their front feet which on examination will be found to be very hot. Animals will have a tendency to stand and lie with their front feet stretched out in front of them.

Treatment

A course of cortisone type drugs will relieve the pain but affected animals take a long time to recover.

Prevention

Avoid overfeeding, especially with very high protein feeds. Make sure that animals that are being fed hard get adequate exercise.

Calves with broken legs

If an animal is so lame that it carries the leg all the time and won't put any weight on it whatsoever, there is a fair chance that the leg is broken.

Breaks below the knee

If a young calf breaks a leg below the knee, a splint should be put on it straight away to save any further damage to the muscles or nerves. This is best done by first stretching the leg to release any trapped nerves, then having padded it with cotton wool, put a splint on either side, wrap black agricultural tape round it to keep the splints in place until such time as you can get the vet to put the leg in plaster. Splints can be made by splitting a piece of plastic power drive cover long ways, and putting a half on each side or using strips cut from plastic guttering.

Breaks above the knee

In cases where the break is high up in the hip or shoulder, these are sometimes best left alone, provided the calf can be housed somewhere where it can't run about too much. The calf will usually carry the leg for about eight weeks before putting any weight on it. It will be another four weeks before it is sound.

Haematomas

Symptoms

Sometimes called blood blisters, these are the result of an animal get-

ting a bump, causing a large amount of fluid to gather under the skin.
Treatment
If treated straight away, by hosing the affected part with cold water
for fifteen minute sessions, three or four times a day, this will sometimes reduce the swelling.

It is very tempting to pierce the swelling and drain the fluid, but in
my experience this often leads to infection and scarring, whereas if
left alone it may take a long time for the swelling to go down, but
when it does there will seldom be any marks left.

Retained cleansing (afterbirth)
Never attempt to remove the cleansing by pulling it externally, as
this will not only distress the animal but may cause haemorrhaging. If the animal has not cleansed after three days call in the vet.
Where there is a high incidence of retained cleansings veterinary
advice should be sought to determine the cause.

Scouring
Scouring in adult cattle
The most common cause of scouring in adult cattle is over-eating.
Adult cattle scouring for no apparent reason should seen by the vet
to ensure that they are not suffering from bovine viral dioheria.

Scouring in yearling cattle
Gut worms are usually the most common cause of scouring in yearling cattle.

Scouring in young calves.
This is usually caused by calves getting too much milk, especially if
the calf has been separated from its mother for a long period and
then gorges itself when it gets back to her. Viral scours in young
calves can be devastating, and unless they are treated early, mortality can be high can be high.

Treatment
A range of scour medication is available (be advised by your vet.)
Calves that are scouring will suffer from de-hydration. Preparations
such as lactade which are high in blood salts help recovery.

Prevention

Avoid mixing bought in calves with the established herd. Vaccinations are available that can be given to cows six weeks before they calve. These build up immunity in the cow which is passed on to the calf through the colostrum in its mothers milk.

Poisons
Yew

This tree is very poisonous to cattle with them dying within a very short time of eating even very small amounts of it. Most cases of yew poisoning are caused by neighbours throwing hedge clippings over the fence where cattle can get access to it.

Treatment
Animals usually die before they can be treated.

Prevention
Make sure that cattle don't have access to areas where there are yew trees. Neighbours who have yew trees in their gardens should be made aware of how deadly it is to cattle.

Acorns
Cattle can often eat a lot of acorns without coming to any harm, so long as they are getting plenty of grass and other food as well. It's usually when they are short of other food and eat large quantities of acorns that poisoning occurs.

Symptoms
Acorn poisoning affects an animal's liver and kidneys and is often difficult to diagnose because it is usually some time after eating the acorns that the animal becomes ill.

Treatment
In most cases, by the time animal shows signs of illness, the damage to the liver and kidneys is beyond repair.

Lead poisoning
Symptoms
Lead poisoning affects the animals nervous system. Animals will have fits or suddenly go blind. They can also have severe scouring

and gut pains.
Cause
The commonest cause of lead poisoning is from licking broken car batteries or old lead pipes.

Treatment
Animals seldom recover, by the time the condition is diagnosed, it is usually too far advanced to be cured.

Over-Eating
Cause
This is usually the result of animals getting access to stores of concentrates, barley, potatoes, sugar beet or such like and eating so much that they either have bloat or become very sick.

Treatment
While it may be possible to save affected animals by immediate veterinary attention, it is not uncommon to have high mortality among the others. Where individual valuable animals are affected the vet may be able to do an operation; open up the animal's stomach and empty it.

Prevention
It is good practice to make a habit of shutting all doors of feed stores and be aware of the possibility of cattle breaking out and getting access to other stores or clamps.

Small equipment

There are one or two bits and pieces of equipment that, although not absolutely essential, nevertheless make work a lot easier and save a lot of time. These include a calving aid, electric fencer, pressure washer and hair blower. Other things needed are a show box, leather, or white cotton halters, show stick, brushes, ordinary combs and pin-tooth combs.

Calving Aid
In my opinion a calving aid is an "absolute necessity" in any herd for the simple reason that with one, even the most slightly built person can help animals calve.. Calving aids come in all shapes and sizes. My personal preference is for the simple ones that have a single shaft

with a tee bar at the top and a ratchet that pulls each leg alternately.

Electric fencers

When buying an electric fencer to energise permanent electric fences always buy a heavy duty unit, powered off the mains, and capable of energising long stretches of fence, as these are effective even though the grass has grown up and may be "shorting" on them. Battery powered electric fencers are equally effective, but only so long as the batteries are at full power. It is all to easy to forget to keep them charged up.

Pressure washers

There is a large range of pressure washers on the market, with prices usually reflecting their capabilities. The smallest ones, usually sold for washing cars, are alright for washing the odd beast or two and have the advantage of being fairly lightweight making it possible to take them with you to shows. When large numbers of animals have to be washed on a regular basis, a medium sized one is best, as it can be run all day with no fear of it overheating. It is essential that it has the facility for spraying on shampoo. This type of washer can also be used for washing buildings and machinery.

Hair blowers

Blowers are useful for getting cattle dried quickly at shows and sales. The American type that blow hot air are the best, as they produce a large volume of air at a reasonable pressure.

Show boxes

The thing to remember about show boxes, is that someone has to lift them. For this reason, if you have a lot of gear, it is far better to have two medium size boxes, than one very large one. It is also an advantage if they are slim enough to go through the little side door in a cattle wagon.

Show sticks

Show sticks are another of the ideas brought over from America and although I have shown cattle all my life without one, I must admit they are useful for positioning the animal's feet when taking photographs and for scratching their bellies to get them to stand still when they are in a line-up being judged. The telescopic ones, although usually bulkier, have the advantage that they can put in

the show box.
Handling equipment
Whether the herd size is to be three or three hundred animals, the first priority when starting any cattle enterprise is to have the facilities to handle them. This should consist of a pen, race, and crush, through which cattle can be run for testing or dosing without injuring themselves, or the people involved.

With good handling facilities vets can test about fifty cattle an hour, but it is not uncommon for them to spend a whole morning trying to test five, on a farm with poor facilities, where animals jump over gates, or burst pens.

Ideally races and crushes should be installed in such a position, that the animals can be handled from either side, as this allows the handlers to work on the one side and the vets on the other. They should also be situated in a position where the animals go through them on their way back to their pens, or out to the field.

Buildings

To ensure that all developing pedigree animals, get every chance to reach their their full potential without being bullied by their elders, there is usually a need to make some alterations to existing buildings or to put up new ones to keep the various groups separate.

Before any building work is done take the time to study the layout of buildings at established herds; This will give you some idea as to which type will be best suited to your needs. For while specialist advice is available for buildings, most of it concerns the needs of dairy or commercial cattle, which are different from that of pedigree beef.

Because of the high cost of erecting new buildings or altering existing ones, ensure that everyone involved, including the stockman, fully understands the designs before building begins, Otherwise, as I have seen time and time again, it is not until building has commenced, that design faults may be noticed. It is worth remembering that if design faults are changed after building has commenced, the cost can rise considerably, as the builder has you at his mercy. The first consideration when erecting a new building or altering an existing one, is easy access for feeding and mucking out, which is usually done by tractors fitted with hydraulic loaders. so always allow plenty of room for them turning, and at least twelve feet headroom above doorways.

When erecting buildings for cattle always ensure that they have adequate ventilation. Walls built with concrete blocks to a height of eight feet, with the space between the top of the wall and the eaves filled in with four inch by three quarter inch boarding,fitted perpendicularly, with a two inch space between them (known in the trade as Yorkshire Boarding) are ideal.

Yards for adult cattle

Yard sizes are based on the length of trough space, relative to the depth of lying area. When building for pedigree cattle it is always best to err on the generous side in the lying area.

Adult cattle of the larger continental breeds need about two and a half feet trough space per animal, this works out at 16 animals to each 40 feet wide bay, Bays about 45 feet deep give sufficient lying space, and room for a small pen where the calves can get a bite of feeding.

Try wherever possible to keep the inside walls of the building flush with the edge of any stanchions, to save cows from damaging their hip bones when they are fighting. Water troughs should be positioned in corner of the yards for the same reason.

Yards for young stock

Young stock always seem to do best in south facing yards that have open fronts, with a concrete outrun between the bedded area and the feeding troughs, which can be scraped out with a tractor every two or three days. Having plenty of fresh air reduces the risk of pneumonia, while the bare concrete helps to keep their feet hard, with less risk of problems than when running on muck all the time.

The only trouble with bare concrete is that if young bulls start fighting they can scrub their feet badly and go lame. I find that pens with a covered area of 20 feet wide by 30 ft deep with a 15 feet out-run in front of the troughs to be about the ideal size. The yards should be constructed so that when the gates of the outrun are shut for scraping, they shut the cattle in the bedded area.

Calving pens

Unless you are sure of their temperament, cows with newborn calves should not be put in boxes with solid walls and only one exit, as it can be dangerous if the cow gets between you and the door.

Pens 15 feet wide by 20 feet deep are a nice size for cows with small calves, dividing them by three rail barriers makes it easier to catch any nasty cows from the adjoining pen. It avoids having to go in beside them.

Pens for young bulls

In the days when labour was plentiful and cheap, young bulls were kept in separate boxes and mucked out every day by hand. This was very labour intensive. Nowadays most breeders with large herds run their young bulls in batches, splitting them into smaller groups as they get older. Wherever possible, pens for young bulls should be situated right out of sight of the females, otherwise they will be constantly getting worked up every time something is bulling, causing them to start riding one another, and fighting.

Pens for stock bulls

Most people who pass an old bull's pen like to put their hand in and try to stroke its head. Therefore it is best to situate the pen somewhere out of the way, otherwise, if the bull is temperamental, the constant teasing will soon make him worse. Unlike young bulls, stock bulls should be kept in pens where they can see the cows, as this will stimulate them, and make them more eager to serve.

Safety barriers or escape exits should be incorporated into the design of pens for old bulls, to give the stockman a chance of escape if he is attacked. Bear in mind that some insurers may be reluctant to pay out compensation to anyone injured by a bull in a pen not fitted with them.

Fences
Boundary fences
In order not to lose stock, or be sued for any accidents or damage

done by stock that stray, it is vital that boundary fences are well maintained. Hedges, no matter how stock proof they may appear, should not be relied on to keep in cattle. They should be supplemented by a fence constructed with either two or three strands of barbed wire.

If the fences have to keep in sheep as well, five strands of plain wire with a strand of barb on top, stapled on to pressure-treated wooden posts six feet apart, is best. But if only cattle are involved, three strands of barbed wire fitted on posts nine feet apart, is usually sufficient. As straining posts are the most important part of any fence, make sure they are put in deep enough and firm enough to take the strain, and where ever possible erect the fence in a straight line between them.

On farms where there are existing post and rail fences, it is advisable to erect a single strand electric fence in front of them. This saves them being damaged by cattle rubbing on them, especially, if the cattle are of the larger continental breeds.

Permanent electric fences

Because of the very high cost of conventional fencing, many stockmen are now turning to permanent electric fences. Provided they are properly erected and well maintained, they are extremely efficient, but should not be relied on for boundary fences.

It is always best to run permanent electric fences from a control unit that gets its power from the mains electricity, rather than a battery. The control unit should be fitted in a position where you are passing it regularly, in this way there is less chance of a "short" going unnoticed. Electric fences should carry a warning notice if there is any chance of the public coming in contact with them.

When fencing against a hedge or conventional fence a single strand of wire fitted one metre high, on wooden posts 20 metres apart is usually sufficient. Where fields are to be split and there are going to be cattle on both sides of the fence, two strands of wire fitted on posts 12 metres apart should be used.

Green fences

This is a system for splitting fields, where two single strand electric fences are erected six feet apart. This allows a strip of grass to grow between the fences, making them more easily seen by animals running at speed.

Temporary electric fences
When erecting temporary electric fences a single strand of wire fitted on posts 20 yards apart is usually sufficient. It is often handiest to energise them by a battery powered unit.

Make-believe fences
Cattle that are trained to electric fences are very wary when they see anything that resembles an electric wire, so when moving cattle around the buildings, it is often possible to get them to go where you want, by simply tying string across any gaps.

Crossing gateways
Crossing gateways is best done by burying the cables underground, rather than suspending them overhead, where they will get in the way of tractors. Specially insulated underground cables are available for this purpose and if fitted inside a length of polythene pipe this will give them added protection and make replacement easier if the need arises.

Electric gates
If electric wires are used for gates, install them in such a way that when they are hooked off and laid on the ground they are "dead", ie they carry no power.

Isolators
Each field should have a separate isolator switch, enabling repairs to be carried out with only the field you are working on switched off. Isolators also make it easier to trace faults, in that each field can be switched off individually.

Breeds

National Cattle Breeders Association

R Kershaw Dalby, Lawford Grange, Rugby, Warwickshire CV23 9HG Tel: 01788 565264

Aberdeen Angus

The Aberdeen Angus Cattle Society, Pedigree House, 6 Kings Place, Perth, Scotland PH2 8AD Tel: 01738 622477

Record price bull   60,000 gns Vendor Sir Torquil & Lady Munro
Record price female   11,000 gns Vendor AB McQuater
Average price for bulls at main spring sale 1995 .... £3025
Average price for bulls at main autumn sale 1995 .... £2390
Average weight at 400 day for bulls .... 484 kg
Average weight at 400 day for females .... 356 kg
Royal Show 1996 Heaviest adult bull .... 1457 kg
Royal Show 1996 Heaviest adult female .... 1072 kg
Royal Show 1996 Average weight adult bulls .... 1224 kg
Royal Show 1996 Average weight adult females .... 907 kg

Beef Shorthorn

Beef Shorthorn Cattle Society, c/o Dairy Shorthorn Cattle Society, Fourth Street, NAC Stoneleigh, Warwickshire, CV8 2LG
Tel: 01203 696549

Record price bull 14,500 gns   Vendor R L Smith
Record price female *Not available*
Average price for bulls at main spring sale 1995 .... £2356
Average price for bulls at main autumn sale 1995 .... £1000
Average weight at 400 day for bulls .... 486 kgs
Average weight at 400 day for females .... 373 kgs
Royal Show 1996 Heaviest adult bull .... 1409 kgs
Royal Show 1996 Heaviest adult female .... 1096 kgs
Royal Show 1996 Average weight adult males .... 1261 kgs
Royal Show 1996 Average weight adult females .... 906 kgs

Blonde d'Aquitaine

The Blonde d'Aquitaine Breeders Society, 16 Market Place, Faringdon, Oxon, SN7 7HS Tel: 01367 242315
Record price bull   7000 gns   Vendor JC Lewis
Record price female   6800 gns   Vendor E&A Stubbs
Average price for bulls at main spring sale 1995 ....£2467
Average price for bulls at main autumn sale 1995 .... £1906
Average weight at 400 day for bulls ....544 kgs
Average weight at 400 day for females ....421 kgs
Royal Show 1996 Heaviest adult bull ....1377 kgs
Royal Show 1996 Heaviest adult female............................1025 kgs
Royal Show 1996 Average weight adult bulls......................1190 kgs
Royal Show 1996 Average weight females..........................1001 kgs

British Charolais.

British Charolais Cattle Society, Avenue M, NAC Stoneleigh, Warwickshire, CV8 2LZ Tel: 01203 697222

Record price bull   54,000 gns. Vendor DE Evans
Record price female   27,000 gns Vendor Mr & Mrs GL Lyster
Average price for bulls at main spring sale 1995 ....£3648
Average price for bulls at main autumn sale 1995................£3992
Average weight at 400 day for bulls ....622 kgs
Average weight at 400 day for females..............................463 kgs
Royal Show 1996 Heaviest adult bull..................................1530 kgs
Royal Show 1996 Heaviest adult female ....1267 kgs
Royal Show 1996 Average weight adult bulls ....1440 kgs
Royal Show 1996 Average weight adult females ....1150 kgs

Hereford

Hereford Cattle Society, Hereford House, 3 Offa Street, Hereford. HR1 2LL Tel: 01432 2272057

Record price bull 27,000 gns   Vendor E.L. Lewis
Record price female 8,500 gns
Average price for bulls at main spring sale 1995 ....£ 1350
Average price for bulls at main autumn sale 1995........................£
Average weight at 400 day for bulls ....540 kgs
Average weight at 400 day for females ....396 kgs
Royal Show 1996 Heaviest adult bull..................................1330 kgs
Royal Show 1996 Heaviest adult female ....903 kgs

Royal Show 1996 Average weight adult bulls ....1270 kgs
Royal Show 1996 Average weight adult females ....643 kgs

Limousin

The British Limousin Cattle Society, National Agricultural Centre, Kenilworth, Warwicks CV8 2RA. Tel: 01203 696500.

Record price bull   35,000 gns. Vendor Mr Robert Graham
Record price female   29,000 gns Vendor Mr John Powner
Average price for bulls at main spring sale 1995 ....£ 2895
Average price for bulls at main autumn sale 1995................£ 2860
Average weight at 400 day for bulls ....537 kgs
Average weight at 400 day for females...............................396 kgs
Royal Show 1996 Heaviest adult bull ....1533 Kgs
Royal Show 1996 Heaviest adult female ....1005 kgs
Royal Show 1996 Average weight adult bulls ....1231 kgs
Royal Show 1996 Average weight adult females.................991 kgs

Simmental

The Secretary, British Simmental Cattle Society, National Agricultural Centre. Kenilworth, Warwicks CV8 2lR.
Tel: 01203 696513.

Record price bull 18000 gns   Vendor F.C. Baker.
Record price female 11000 gns   Vendor R. Luness
Average price for bulls at main spring sale 1995 ....£2554
Average price for bulls at main autumn sale 1995.................£2763
Average weight at 400 day for bulls ....618 kgs
Average weight at 400 day for females...............................437 kgs
Royal Show 1996 Heaviest adult bull................................1429 kgs
Royal Show 1996 Heaviest adult female ....1100 kgs
Royal Show 1996 Average weight adult bulls ....1394 kgs
Royal Show 1996 Average weight adult females ....1016 kgs

Belgian Blue

The Belgian Blue Cattle Society, Coleshill Lodge, Litchfield Road, Abbots Bromley, Nr Rugley Staffs. Tel: 01283-840315.

Record price bull   10500 gns.   Vendor. D Williams.
Record price female 9200 gns   Vendor Ashton.
British White
The Secretary, The British White Cattle Society, PO Box 35, Kenilworth, Warwickshire CV8 2XE. Tel: 01203 696523
Record price bull   1600 gns   Vendor South Elham Hall Farms
Record price female   1770 gns   Vendor Delamore Farms Ltd

Chianina
Chianina Cattle Breed Society, 44 Wallshed Way, Church Aston, Newport, Shropshire. TF10 9JF. Tel: 01952 812970.

Record price bull   *Not Available.*
Record price female *Not Available.*

Devon
Devon Cattle Breeders Society, Barn Lane Farm, Stoke River, Barnstaple, Devon. EX32 7LD. Tel: 01598 710495.

Record price bull   9000 gns   Vendor Capper Farms
Record price female   1220 gns   Vendor DF Dawn

Galloway
The Galloway Cattle Society, 15 New Market Street, Castle Douglas, Dumfries, Scotland. Tel: 01556 502753.

Record price bull   22,000 gns. Vendor G. Wilson
Record price female   4000 gns   Vendor M. C. Brown
Record price female   4000 gns   Vendor W.F.E Forbes

Belted Galloway
Secretary JMC Rutherford, Rutherford Lodge, Kelso, Roxburghshire. TD5 8NW. Tel: 083 52 3757.

Record price bull   5,200 gns
Record price female   11,500 gns

Gasconne
Gasconne Cattle Society, 27 Pasturelands Drive, Billington, Whalley, Lancs. BB7 9LP. Tel: 012254 823688

Record price bull   *Not Available*
Record price female *Not Available*

Gelbvieh

British Gelbvieh Cattle Society, Paddocks Farm, Taylors Lane, Buckden, Cambs. PE18 9UW. Tel: 01480 810743.

Record price bull   *Not Available*
Record price female *Not Available*

Highland

Highland Cattle Society, 59 Drumlanrig Road, Thornhill, Dumfries. DG3 5l7. Tel: 01848-330438.

Record price bull   20.000 gns. Vendor D. Mac Gillvary
Record price female 12000 gns Vendor Leys Fold

Lincoln Red

Lincoln Red Cattle Society, Lincolnshire Showground, Grange-de-Lings, Lincoln. LN2 2NA. Tel: 01522 544544.

Record price bull   4400 gns   Vendor Manley Farms
Record price female 1200 gns   Vendor F E Read & Son

Longhorn

The Secretary, The Longhorn Cattle Society, Peel House, 14 West Street, Shipston on Stour, Warwickshire. CV36 4HD. Tel: 01608 662967.

Record price bull   3,600 gns   Vendor P Close
Record price female 3,400 gns   Vendor P Close

Maine Anjou

Maine Anjou Cattle Society, The Old Farm House, Brook End, Little Dunmow, Essex. CM6 3AA. Tel: 01371 820074.

Record price bull   *Not Available*
Record price female *Not Available*

Murray Grey

Ms C Evans, Murray Grey Cattle Society, c/o National Agricultural Centre, Stoneleigh, Warwickshire. CV8 2TZ. Tel: 01203 696989.

Record price bull   *Not Available*
Record price female   *Not Available*
Piemontese
Piemontese Cattle Society, 7 Fisher Street, Carlisle, Cumbria.
CA3 8RF. Tel: 01228 818022.

Record price bull   *Not Available*
Record price female   *Not Available*

Red Poll
PR Davies, The Secretary, The Red Poll Cattle Society, Market Hill,
Woodbridge, Suffolk. Tel: 01394 380643.

Record price bull   *Not Available*
Record price female   *Not Available*

Romagnola
British Romagnola Cattle Society, 26 York Place, Perth. PN2 8EH.
Tel: 01738 623780.

Record price bull   *Not Available*
Record price female   *Not Available*

Salers
Saler Cattle Society, Brookhouse Farm, Norbury, Whitchurch,
Shropshire. SY13 4HY. Tel: 01948 667223.

Record price bull   *Not Available*
Record price female   *Not Available*

South Devon
South Devon Herdbook Society, 24 Courtenay Park, Newton Abbot,
South Devon. TQ12 2HB. Tel: 01626 331144.

Record price bull 5,600 gns   Vendor RRB Harvey
Record price Female 3,400 gns   Vendor Lord Courtanay

Sussex
Sussex Cattle Society, Station Road, Robertsbridge, East Sussex.
TN32 5DG. Tel: 01580 880105.

Record price bull   *Not Available*
Record price female *Not Available*
Welsh Black
Welsh Black Cattle Society, Bangor Street, Caernarvon, Gwynedd.
LL5 1AP. Tel: 01286 672391.

Record price bull   8,000 gns   Vendor Hywel M Jenkins
Record price female 5,600 gns   Vendor Lady D Gibson Watt

Bits and pieces

Vets
Vets, like many other things, come in all shapes and sizes; good; bad; and indifferent. For this reason it is worth while shopping around to find a practice where at least one of the partners is keen on working with large animals, as it gives great peace of mind to know when you call out your vet that they are interested in your stock and know exactly what they are doing, especially when they are pregnancy testing; calving; or doing caesarean operations.

Don't complain if the vet calls during your lunch hour, There may come a time when there is an emergency and you will expect him to get out of his bed in the middle of the night.

Pregnancy diagnosis (P.D.)
Vets that are good at pregnancy testing prefer to internally examine the animals when they between six and twelve weeks pregnant. After this stage the weight of the embryo pulls the womb over the pelvis making pregnancy diagnosis more difficult. Pregnancy can also be diagnosed by means of ultra- sonic scanning.

Heifers that are twin to a bull
It is very rare for heifers that are twin to a bull to breed, as most have either; under-developed; or non existent ovaries and wombs. In all the years I have been a stockman I have only ever had one that bred.

Tranquillisers
It is forbidden to give animals tranquillisers at sales. Any animal

testing positive to tranquillisers or performance enhancing drugs after a sale, will render the transaction null and void. The vendor will also be responsible for the costs involved. and more than likely be disciplined or suspended by the breed society concerned.

It is worth remembering that tranquillisers such as ACP can be identified in blood samples for three weeks after being administered.

Cheating and malpractices

Whenever there is competition, or money to be made, there is always someone who can't resist cheating, and so it is with cattle breeding.

Thankfully there are very few breeders or stockmen who participate in malpractices these days, but there are still a few who cheat the ages of their calves. Breed Societies have been taking a much tougher line with anyone cheating ages over the last couple of years, with the result that breeders are beginning to realise that it is not worth getting caught, and having all their calves expelled from the herd book.

Etiquette when visiting other herds

If a fellow breeder invites you to look round his herd, and there is nobody about when you arrive, don't start nosing around looking at his animals , wait until he arrives. It may be that as you go round you may come across things; or may discuss problems; that he does not want to be made public. Therefore out of courtesy don't get on the phone and gossip to other breeders about what you have seen, or pull the cattle to pieces.

Young breeders stock judging competitions

These have become very popular, and are an excellent way of training the judges of the future, provided they are trained by top breeders and stockmen.

Young breeders cattle handling competitions

Cattle handling competitions give youngsters an opportunity to learn how to handle cattle in the show ring and how to cope with competition. The one reservation I have is, that in some breeds, youngsters get carried away with themselves and act like prima donnas, only handling well trained cattle in the show ring, and never learning the basics, like mucking out; washing mucky hips, or how to handle a rougher going animal.

Judges of these competitions should not only take into consideration how the competitors handle their cattle when they are in front of the judge, but how they handle them all the time they are in the ring. It is also worth while putting some of the top ones down the line a bit in the preliminary line up, just to see whether they work hard enough to get to the top of the class, or accept defeat.

Showing high priced animals

Before showing high priced animals, especially ones that were champion at major sales and purchased as stock bulls, the question should be asked; what is there to gain? In my view, showing is a means of publicity, and as these animals have had their day of glory and all the publicity that goes with it, it is often far better to let people remember them as they were on the day they were champion, rather than to drag them out to summer shows the following year and get them beaten.

Many breeders over the years have had stock bulls that were very popular, with a lot of semen being sold from them, only to kill the whole trade by showing the bull out of condition, resulting in it being placed at the bottom of the class.

Most high priced animals are sold at their peak of condition, and aged under two year old. If they are to be shown again it is usually best to give them a rest from feeding and a chance to "grow on' for a couple of years, before showing them again as four year olds. But in fairness to the animal and the person from whom it was purchased, the animal should only be shown if it is in such condition that it has a good chance of winning major shows.

Retiring show cows

In fairness to good show cows they should be retired when they are at the top of the tree. It's far better to have people remember them as good cows, rather than showing them when they are past their prime and people remembering them as old crocks.

Care of newly acquired animals

Bulls purchased at sales, are best housed on their own when they arrive at their new home, preferably in a pen in sight of other cattle. Their diet should be restricted to hay and water for the first couple of days to give their stomach a chance to get working properly again after their journey. Feeding can then be introduced over the next few days according to appetite.

Newly acquired females will also benefit from being housed on their own until they are turned out to grass, Otherwise if they are put in with an established group there is every chance that they will be bullied relentlessly by all the members of the established group.

When several females have been purchased from different herds they can be penned together as a group, there may some fighting initially until they sort out their "pecking" order, after which they should settle down without too much bullying.

Behaviour patterns in cattle
There is a strict "pecking" order within groups of cattle in a herd as can be seen from the position in which they line up at the trough at feeding time. For this reason it is always best to stick to a set routine when giving them their food.

There also seems to be a close bond between some members within groups of cattle, especially in the continental breeds. It is not uncommon for individual animals to bawl for days when they have been moved from one group to another. This is also noticeable at shows, when some of the group are taken out for showing or parades, the others don't settle until they return.

Cattle are easily trained. Herds of up to sixty cows can be trained to go into their allocated stall in a cow shed and when tied in pairs soon learn to move over (one each way) to let you get up between them.

Making halters
It is well worth learning how to make your own rope halters. Not only are they cheaper, but you can make them the size to fit your needs. Most experienced stockmen make their own halters, and if asked will willingly show you how.

The following Photographs are examples of animals ready for the judging ring at either Summer shows or Breed Society sales.

Aberdeen Angus (Native).

Beef Shorthorn (Native).

Hereford (Native).

Highland (Native).

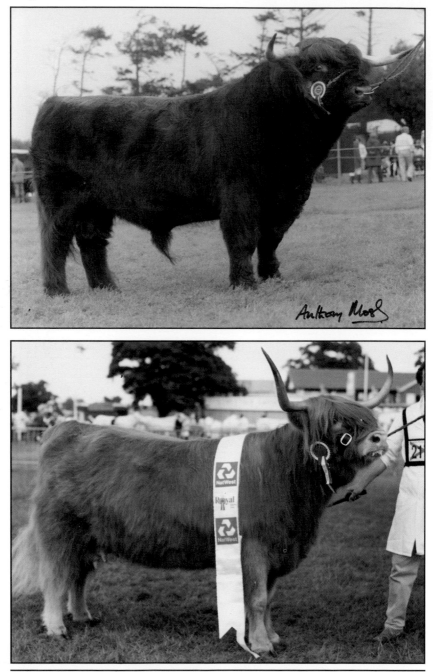

British Charolais (Continental).

British Simmental (Continental).

Limousin (Continental).

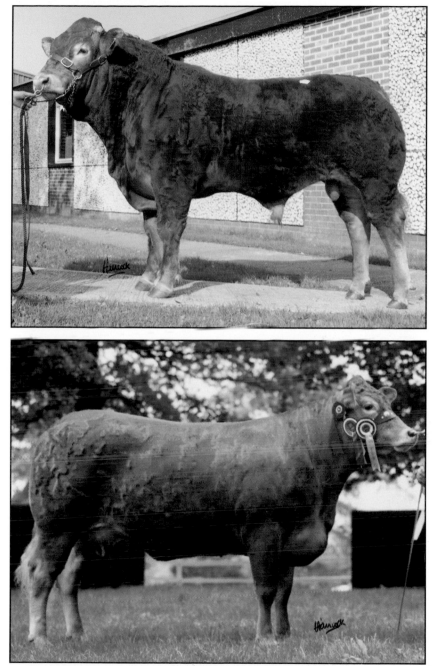

Blonde dAquitaine (Continental).

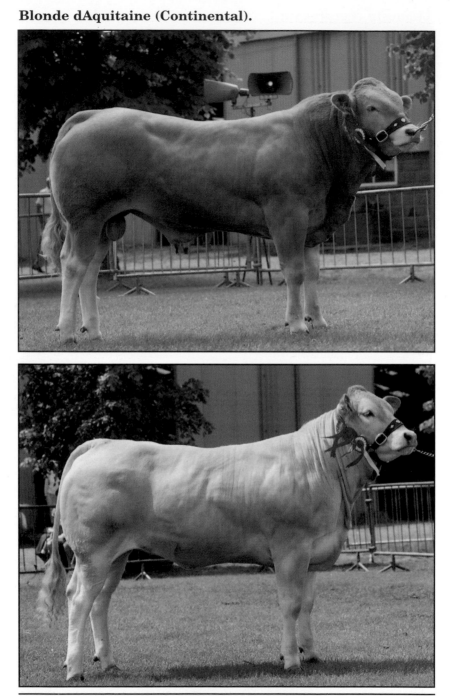

Index

Illustrations, diagrams and photographs